Laurence A. Brown Jr.   from   Sarah Fraur Robbins –

THE HOUSE SPARROW

A NEW NATURALIST SPECIAL VOLUME

The aim of THE NEW NATURALIST series is to interest the general reader in the wild life of Britain by recapturing the inquiring spirit of the old naturalists. The Editors believe that the natural pride of the British public in their native fauna and flora, to which must be added concern for their conservation, is best fostered by maintaining a high standard of accuracy combined with clarity of exposition in presenting the results of modern scientific research. The volumes in the main series deal with large groups of animals and plants, with the natural history of particular areas or habitats in Britain, and with certain special subjects. THE NEW NATURALIST SPECIAL VOLUMES, on the other hand, cover, in greater detail, a single species or group of species. In both the main series and special volumes the animals and plants are described in relation to their homes and habitats, and are portrayed in their full beauty with the help of both colour and monochrome photographs.

Editors

James Fisher, M.A.
John Gilmour, M.A., V.M.H.
Sir Julian Huxley, M.A., D.SC., F.R.S.
L. Dudley Stamp, C.B.E., D.LITT., D.SC.

Photographic Editor
Eric Hosking, F.R.P.S.

Male house sparrow: without his only too frequent coating of city grime, the cock house sparrow is a handsome bird with his black and chestnut; the bill is black in the breeding season. (*E. Hosking*)

THE NEW NATURALIST

THE
HOUSE SPARROW

by
D. SUMMERS-SMITH

With a colour frontispiece
32 photographs in black and white
and 36 text figures

COLLINS
ST. JAMES'S PLACE, LONDON
1963

© D. Summers-Smith, 1963
Printed in Great Britain
by Willmer Brothers & Haram Ltd., Birkenhead
for Collins Clear-Type Press
London and Glasgow

The Sparrow

The viewpoint of the Sparrow
Is arrogant and narrow,
He *knows* that he excels.
He is selfishly obsessed;
He would not give an ostrich best.
His children leave their shells
Puffed to their very marrows
With pride at being sparrows.

Marie de la Welch

CONTENTS

LIST OF PLATES

LIST OF TEXT FIGURES

EDITORS' PREFACE

"Far too well-known to need any description of its appearance or habits." Such was the opinion of Alfred Newton of the house sparrow—Newton, the founder of our British Ornithologists' Union and in a good sense of modern scientific ornithology.

Newton was a formidable scholar, who has to be forgiven so unscholarly a remark: he would have thoroughly appreciated the skill and new scholarship with which Mr. Summers-Smith has proved him wrong.

The most abundant bird in the world is certainly the domestic fowl, whose population probably approximates to that of its three billion human masters. Next must come a wild bird, and it is probably the house sparrow (possibly the starling), which has in late years spread so widely over our planet's surface as a consequence of human introduction. It is an incredibly successful, plastic, opportunist weaver bird that can find an ecological niche almost anywhere that agricultural man has; and it is high time that it had a monographer. We introduce Mr. Summers-Smith's book with pride and pleasure; for it is a most professional and readable job that sets a new standard. It will be not merely used by the researchers of the future: it will be built upon. It is a full conspectus, from which every kind of naturalist can gain information and inspiration.

The ethologist will enjoy the results of the writer's eleven-year study of sparrow behaviour, half in the country, half in the suburbs: a study conducted with passion and thoroughness, and with a fine regard for the published work of others and for comparison with other races and species of *Passer domesticus* and its genus.

The migration student will appreciate a classic study of a classically sedentary bird, most economically arranged; unlike some other good scholars Mr. Summers-Smith has a flair for distilling the essential information and presenting it crisply and tidily. His chapter on disease and parasites is a masterpiece of presentation, and perhaps overmodest in its conclusion that little is really known about the hazards of the house sparrow's life. Certainly an insurance assessor who follows his chapter on expectation of life and mortality could work out better life tables and figures for this common bird at all its seasons and ages than he could for some populations of his own species.

The ecologist will be delighted with the material on population, with some new and interesting figures which show that its numbers in England, Wales and Scotland are certainly larger than was previously supposed. Mr. Summers-Smith's investigations into the distribution of the house sparrow and its allies have been conducted with the eyes of an evolutionary ecologist, are embellished with fine accurate maps, take note of Pleistocene ice-age history and work out in fascinating detail all the recent changes in the bird's range, both natural and as the consequence of introduction.

The writer ends his book with dissertations on the sparrow's economy—its relationship with man, which lead him to a final chapter on the secret of its success, in which he does not try to escape the conclusion that the bird is, for a bird, relatively intelligent, and may be capable of solving some problems intuitively and not by trial and error learning.

Mr. Summers-Smith writes that he finds it very difficult to say whether he loves the house sparrow, though he admits that life, for him, would be very dull without it. Editorially, we unhesitatingly regard him as a sparrow lover. No other could have been spurred, through more than a decade, to contribute so much to the store of human knowledge on one species and its allies, and gather the rest of it, in its well-chosen essentials, into one volume. There have been many good monographs in our *New Naturalist* series, and this stands among the very best, a model of balanced presentation, scientific scholarship and good style.

THE EDITORS

AUTHOR'S PREFACE

I HAVE become very conscious when writing this book that it is only a half-story. So much is published these days about birds in so many publications that it becomes difficult for even the professional biologist to keep in touch with it; as an amateur I have not even tried to make the attempt and have confined my reading of the literature to works specifically relating to sparrows—in this restricted field alone I have collected over a thousand references. This means that comparisons with other species are lacking and that in more specialised fields, for example, behaviour, my contribution is very inadequate; still I hope that the descriptions given are sufficiently accurate to be of value to those more competent than I to make use of them and yet sufficiently complete to bring the bird to life for the more general reader.

The house sparrow is of almost universal distribution so that certain seasonally-dependent activities, such as breeding, moulting and so on, occur at different times of the year in different parts of the world; most of the observations I shall report have been made in the British Isles and it can be assumed that this is the case unless specific mention is made to the contrary.

Not the least of the pleasures I have had from my study of the house sparrow have been the contacts I have made with ornithologists in five continents—the sparrow does not yet occur in Antarctica. So many of these people have helped me wittingly and unwittingly in my study that I cannot begin to mention them by name; if they can see anything of their ideas in the book, I hope this may give them a little satisfaction in place of acknowledgement. It would be churlish, however, not to record my appreciation of what my wife has suffered in the way of disturbance at my early rising, disrupted meals and absence of attention in the evening during the months spent in writing; she has also contributed to the observations and done her best to improve the style of writing and continuity. I should also like to name Mr. L. R. Lewis, who has listened patiently to my ideas on sparrows for over ten years and offered valuable constructive criticism during the writing of the book, Mr. P. J. Stead, who has brought to life so well the postures in his wholly delightful drawings, and finally Miss D. Bell and Mrs. J. Gibson, who were responsible for the line diagrams and distribution maps.

Writing was begun in 1959 and I have attempted to cover the literature on sparrows up to the end of 1958, though I have not hesitated to make use of more recent information that has come to hand. A complete list of references to all authorities quoted would be of interest to only a few confirmed sparrow enthusiasts. Instead I have given a selected bibliography on the house sparrow which I think covers the most significant contributions to our knowledge of the species. Fully annotated versions of the text with a complete bibliography are, however, available for reference at the Alexander Library, Edward Grey Institute, Botanic Garden, Oxford and at the Bird Room, British Museum (Natural History), Cromwell Road, London, S.W.7.

D. SUMMERS-SMITH

CHAPTER I

STUDYING THE HOUSE SPARROW

TO THE inhabitants of Europe, North America and indeed many other parts of the world the house sparrow is probably the most familiar of all birds. Alfred Newton in his Dictionary of Birds published in 1896 wrote of the sparrow: "Far too well-known to need any description of its appearance or habits." Yet over fifty years later after twelve years of watching, reading and thinking about sparrows I know there is much to be learned about them. This of course reflects the change in emphasis in the interest in birds since Newton's time: then it was a question of describing the birds, classifying them and finding out their distribution and nesting habits; now there is much more pre-occupation with their behaviour (ethology) and relationship to their environment (ecology). It must be admitted that the study of the life of the house sparrow has been much neglected and considerably less is known about it than about that of many less accessible birds, the considerable literature that exists on the species being more concerned with its importance as a pest of agriculture than with its behaviour and life history. Even in the last decade more papers have been published on the economic importance of the house sparrow than on all other aspects, though there is a welcome trend for recent studies to be based on a broader biological understanding of the species.

Quite apart from the enjoyment and interest that is to be found in a detailed study of any animal, the house sparrow is particularly worthy of attention. The question of its economic importance to man is still unresolved—but the greatest interest lies in its un-doubted success as an animal and the relationship, unique as far as wild birds are concerned, that it has with man; these two characteristics, as we shall see, are not unconnected. I found too that there were advantages in choosing the house sparrow, particularly when I was able to devote only a limited time to birds: it is readily accessible and no time had to be wasted in travelling to the "study area"; observations could be made before breakfast and in the evenings with the minimum amount of extra effort, and my wife could provide continuity in observations when I was away from home; and lastly any move that I could contemplate having to make for business reasons would be unlikely to separate me from the object of my study—rather it obtrudes in my life and I have been distracted by sparrows outside the various offices I have occupied and have even had a pair nesting in a ventilator in one of them. What is more I have been able to make observations on sparrows on all sorts of holidays at home and abroad and even in such unlikely bird-watching localities as railway stations, the inside of factory buildings and from a dentist's chair! As it happened, five years after starting this study I had to move from the south to the north-east of England; admittedly my house-hunting was influenced by the requirement of breeding house sparrows but this did not impose a severe limitation in choice.

Nevertheless all species have some disadvantages from the point of view of the human observer: not for me the dangers of the high cliffs to which the auk watcher is exposed, nor the physical hardships of the winter estuarine watcher, nor even the self-imposed overtime hours of the nightingale watcher. No! the peculiar difficulty of the house sparrow is its predilection for occupied buildings, the occupiers of which at times resent being looked at through binoculars. This was no great problem in the village where my observations began and my eccentricities were well known, but it became a real difficulty in a suburban area. The problem was largely overcome by carrying out most of my observations on houses in the early hours of the morning before my neighbours had risen, though on occasions when they did get up early their suspicion was even greater and led once to a visit from the police. Another time, when living in the south, I was questioned by the police when carrying out a census in a village where I was not so well known. Both times, I must say, they were most courteous and sympathetic once I had overcome their initial disbelief.

Most of my sparrow watching has been done in these two areas in England—five years in a rural district in Hampshire and six years in the suburbs of a small industrial town in County Durham. As these areas will be frequently mentioned in the following chapters it is appropriate to set the scenes at this stage. My house in Hampshire was one of a group of four on which about fifteen pairs of house sparrows bred. This group of houses was in a populous rural area, mostly permanent grassland interspersed with copses and having only a limited amount of arable land; the habitat was a reasonably stable one and had probably not changed very much for a considerable number of years. Many of the houses had a few chickens and these helped to maintain a moderately high density of sparrows. My suburban study area consisted of a mixture of houses and gardens separated by fields of permanent grass, allotments and parks, and lay about half a mile from an extensive area of mixed farmland. Only a small number of chickens was kept in this district and much of the sparrows' food came from the scraps put out by the local inhabitants. As has happened on the edges of many other towns, this district has been developing during the course of my study and while open spaces still exist a considerable proportion of them have been built on and the suburban boundaries are gradually eroding the farmland. This has had its effect on the wild-life—kestrels, which were formerly regular visitors, are now rarely to be seen—but the general character of the environment has not changed to any great extent. The main difference between these areas, as far as the sparrow is concerned, is that in the rural area the breeding colonies associated with houses were largely separated from each other, whereas in the suburban one my local sparrows formed part of an extensive area of continuous breeding birds. In the built-up area, and possibly in the country one as well, the house sparrow was the commonest breeding species. I very much regret that I have not been able to make comparable observations on a wholly urbanised district and on a completely isolated colony of birds, such as occurs on hill farms in the Pennines and isolated crofts in the Scottish Highlands. Casual observations that I have made in these places, however, suggest that the effect on the behaviour of the sparrow is one of degree rather than of kind. Published information suggests that the same is broadly true of the sparrow in widely different parts of the world.

The chief prop of my observations has been the marking of most of the breeding populations in my study areas with various combinations of coloured plastic rings on their legs so that the different individuals could be distinguished. The marking in the suburban area, where I was catching over two hundred sparrows each year, became something of a problem. Fortunately the house sparrow is sexually dimorphic and has two legs, so that, even with the limited number of colours of rings that I was able to distinguish with field glasses (ten), it was possible to mark a considerable number of birds uniquely. Several of my birds have carried up to three coloured rings, in addition to the serially numbered metal British Museum rings, which I put on all of the sparrows I caught, for five or more years, so that it does not appear that this has been much of a handicap for them.

Sparrows tend to sit down on their tarsi so that the rings are not visible and at times this has led to failure in identification when it would have been most interesting to know the individual concerned; on the other hand they are not skulking in their habits and with a little patience it is normally possible to get a sight of their legs. Odd birds have caused trouble by losing, or possibly deliberately removing, the rings; as they are not easily re-trapped this has led to some confusion, though when regular observations are being made on a comparatively small number of birds it usually becomes possible to identify them, without recourse to the rings, on the basis of small plumage variations and individual tricks of behaviour, so that loss of rings has not been a serious difficulty.

One of the fascinating discoveries of a study like this is the appreciation of just how much individual variation in appearance and character does exist among the animals of one species—the wary and the curious, the timid and the aggressive, the smart and the untidy are all there to be seen; and the disappearance of a familiar character from his place on the roof top is not without its real feeling of loss.

Apart from ringing I interfered as little as I could with the activities of the birds so that the behaviour I observed would be as near normal as possible; for example, the minimum inspection was made of nest-boxes to obtain laying dates and clutch sizes, the nestlings were not weighed nor even ringed, nor were the birds presented with problem situations. This has meant that certain information has been missed and certain observations are incomplete but on balance there have been compensating advantages. However, despite these precautions it would be wrong to claim that my observations were made on perfectly normal populations of birds; there is no doubt that the birds in the colonies that were subjected to continued watching did tend to behave somewhat abnormally. They did not, as might have been expected, come to accept and ignore me. The effect of watching was to make this already wary bird even more wary. I stress the word watching; for example, during the breeding season their behaviour at the nest was different when I was watching them through field glasses from what it was when I was gardening and only casting surreptitious glances towards them. I gave up intensive watching of my local birds at the end of the 1958 breeding season and I am convinced that the attitude of the birds towards me has changed since then— now I am accepted as a normal piece of the landscape and no longer the detested pryer into their private lives, to be viewed with the utmost suspicion.

I have also kept a few house sparrows in an aviary. This has the advantage that the birds can always be kept under observation and it is possible to watch the details of different postures more closely and hear the different calls at short range. These can then be looked for in fully wild birds to confirm that they are not merely peculiar to half-tamed birds in captivity.

This then was the setting for my study. As we shall see, it took me to many distant parts of the world—if not in reality at least in imagination. David Lack writing of ornithological research has said, "If you decide to take up a particular species, and that is one of the most enjoyable of all studies, you must love your bird." I heartily agree that a complete study of one species is particularly satisfying. But do I love the house sparrow? That I find difficult to answer, though I do know that I should find life extremely dull without them as my constant neighbours.

The book is divided into three sections; the first deals with the life history of the house sparrow, the second with its origins and distribution and the third with its ecology. The three following chapters are intended to give a general picture of the bird's day-to-day existence and the way the pattern changes throughout the year. In the first of these we shall start with the young when they leave the nest and follow them through their first year of life until they are ready to breed. The next chapter will continue the story with the adults, to see how their behaviour differs from that of the young birds, and then we shall look at matters like voice, posturing and feeding that go to make up the general pattern of daily living. This will provide the necessary background against which some of the features of the bird's existence can be more fully studied.

CHAPTER 2

THE FIRST YEAR

BY THE *first year* I mean the time from the young birds leaving the nest until they begin to breed, though as house sparrows breed in the year following the one in which they are born, this may not last as much as twelve months. It is convenient to separate this period from the later years as the pattern of behaviour of the juveniles differs somewhat from that of the adults.

In Great Britain the normal breeding season of the house sparrow begins in April and the first eggs are to be found at the end of the month. Hatching and fledging occupies about a month so that the first young of the year are to be seen at the end of May. Observations on the captive sparrows in my aviary showed that fledglings are unable to feed themselves for about a week after leaving the nest, although they attempt to pick up food before this. In the wild the parents continue to feed their young for a further week. The hen, particularly in the early part of the breeding season, normally begins a new brood a few days after the young of the previous brood have fledged; hence it is usually the cock that feeds the young. However, he too soon gets involved in incubating the next clutch and the young are left to their own devices. It is unlikely that the parents and their offspring recognise each other again.

These newly fledged young show no particular attachment to their place of birth and wander around forming loose flocks with others of their kind in waste areas and similar places where there is plenty of food to be found. At this time of year their food appears to be predominantly weed and grass seeds, though they readily accept bread and scraps as well.

This pattern continues through the summer. In rural areas, the flocks, which increase in size as further young birds are fledged, at first gravitate to hay fields, where they feed on grass seeds, and by the end of July to the ripening grain fields. These flocks, which as we shall see in the next chapter are joined by the adults that have finished with breeding, are a familiar sight in the countryside round towns and villages in the late summer; operating from the hedges around the borders of the fields, they cause considerable damage to the crops.

> Whilst thousands in a flock for ever gay
> Loud chirping sparrows welcome on the day,
> And from the mazes of the leafy thorn
> Drop one by one upon the bending corn.
>
> *Bloomfield* 1799

It has been suggested by a number of writers that some of these country flocks may be composed of town sparrows on their summer holidays. However, if we consider the population density of house sparrows and their rate of breeding (as is done in more detail in Chapter 14) it is evident that in most cases the birds could have been drawn from the immediate locality without any of them having moved as much as two or three miles. I have watched these flocks in the two areas where I have particularly studied sparrows. In the rural one there was only one grain field within two miles of my breeding colony, the remainder of the neighbourhood consisting of grassland and copses. This field was about half a mile away and the summer flock there reached a strength of about five hundred birds; many of the young birds that were ringed in my study area were regularly seen at this grain field and there was no evidence from observations or ringing recoveries that any had wandered further away than this. Considering the other breeding colonies located nearby, it seems unlikely that any number of the flock could have come from more than about half a mile away. In my other study area, on the outskirts of a small town, the nearest grain fields were one to two miles away. A number of ringed birds were identified in the flock that formed there, which in this case reached over five thousand birds. The sparrow population in this area was much more dense and a flock of this size could easily have been formed without any of the birds having had to travel more than two or at the most three miles.

What then happens to the birds living in the centres of towns?

The London Natural History Society in their comprehensive study of the Birds of the London Area reported no diminution in the numbers of house sparrows in inner London in the late summer and autumn; similarly E. Hardy found no decrease in the sparrow population in the centre of Liverpool during harvest time. On the other hand, Frl. M. Fallet, who made counts of the total population of sparrows in Kiel, found that about half the young birds moved out of the town during the summer and joined the grain-field flocks of sparrows in the surrounding country. This may not conflict with the above observations, which by merely suggesting that there was no decrease does not deny that a proportion of the young birds could move away. By observation of the break-up of the flocks in the surrounding countryside in the late autumn, Fallet was able to correlate this with an increase of the town population—the population increased by about fifty per cent from September to November—thus showing that the movement of the young birds was only temporary. In large towns it does not seem likely that the birds move far; there is some flocking at richer feeding places, such as the parks and waste places that are to be found at the centres of most of our towns, but it does not appear likely that there is any significant movement to the outskirts as occurred in Kiel. My experience in both the rural and town outskirt areas (and that of F. Preiser in a rural area in southern Germany), where at the end of the summer the breeding areas were almost deserted and few sparrows were to be seen during the daytime, is in marked contrast. In the country areas at this time of year, large roosts, composed mainly of the birds of the year, are formed in hedgerows near the grain fields.

The flocks stay in the fields until the grain is harvested and removed. In bad summers, when the harvest is late and grain is shed before it can be gathered, flocks can still be seen well into October. However, in normal years there is by this time a drift of the young birds back from the fields into the breeding areas. In the rural district, where the number of birds was smaller and a larger proportion of the birds in the flock was colour-ringed, it could be seen that the young birds returned to the breeding areas from which the flock was drawn, though not necessarily to the area in which they were born. This means that the majority of the young birds only moved a mile or two from their birthplace and that little, if any, wider dispersal took place. In the other area, where the numbers involved were very much larger, it was less easy to be certain about the movements of the young birds; however, ringing returns suggest the same behaviour. Some instances of more extensive movement by individual young birds have been recorded (see Chapter 11 and Appendix IV) but this behaviour appears to be somewhat unusual.

F. Preiser, in a rural area near Stuttgart, has examined the behaviour of young birds very carefully by extensive ringing of the local sparrow population (over five thousand young birds were ringed in the years 1952 to 1954). In general, the picture is very similar to that for England: a build-up of large flocks from breeding colonies occurred in the immediately surrounding neighbourhood during the summer and autumn, with a maximum movement of about a mile; after the harvest in the middle of September the birds moved back to the breeding areas. In Kiel, Frl. Fallet found that the break-up of the flocks began in September and was completed at the latest by the middle of November. In Preiser's area the ringing was followed by poisoning campaigns in the winter months. In this way some information was obtained on about seventeen per cent of the ringed birds—a much larger proportion than would normally be the case with small passerines, whose recovery rate is less than one per cent. About ninety-six per cent of the birds about which more information was obtained were scattered at random over the district from which the flock had been drawn; the likelihood of recovery at greater distances is of course less but even then it is clear that only a very small proportion moved away any distance from the area in which they were born.

A further most interesting study, made on the small island of Hilbre in the Cheshire Dee for a period of years by J. D. Craggs, gives a somewhat similar picture. The sparrows, which for the greater part of the year remained close to the house and out-buildings, formed a flock at the end of the breeding season and roamed over the island feeding mostly on weed seeds. In September, the numbers collapsed quite suddenly when approximately half of the young birds disappeared, presumably by dispersal to the mainland; the remaining birds returned then to the more restricted area near the house and autumn flocking was over.

This flocking behaviour provides a useful biological function: it prevents the formation of small inbred populations in a species that tends to be very sedentary in its habits and allows the bird to expand from areas where it is present, into sparrow-poor areas. These may be districts that as a result of changes in the economy have become suitable for house sparrows or districts in which the sparrow population has been reduced by disease. The situation on Hilbre Island, where as shown by complete colour-ringing of the native birds, there were no arrivals of young reared elsewhere, must have led to a high degree of inbreeding; this does appear, however, to be rather exceptional.

When the young birds return to the breeding areas a new form of behaviour is to be seen, particularly on bright sunny mornings from October onwards. I term this "nest-site prospecting". Parties of young birds of both sexes move round investigating holes in roofs and under eaves. As we shall see in the next chapter, the breeding adults have by this time returned to their nest sites. Thus the young birds become familiar with the type of site suitable for nesting and at the same time discover unoccupied holes that may be used for roosting in the winter when the nights become cold. After the return to the colonies the young birds roost communally in the breeding areas in creepers or in trees, but later in the year many take up individual roosting holes. They do not, however, at this stage become attached to any particular breeding colony; not that much movement takes place, but there may be some drifting of individuals between neighbouring breeding areas, particularly when these are contiguous.

Nest-site prospecting carries on into the winter but is less frequent in the short days of December and January, when there is a decline in all sexual behaviour and a corresponding increase in social activities. As soon as the days begin to lengthen and become warmer, prospecting parties are to be seen more regularly. Now the behaviour becomes more purposeful; young cocks adopt unoccupied holes, defend them against other cocks and call persistently until they obtain mates. A second dispersal of young birds may occur at this time of year: the cocks to find nest sites, the hens to look for unmated cocks with nests. It is perhaps significant that almost all the records of house sparrows on offshore islands where they do not breed are in the period March to June (see Chapter 11). Most of the young birds become paired at the beginning of the breeding season or soon afterwards and the juvenile stage of their life can be considered to be over.

CHAPTER 3

ADULT LIFE

IN ONE sense this chapter is a continuation of the last but in another it is not. The first year was an unfolding; this is a repetition of a pattern, which persists from year to year—the bird's behaviour may differ slightly as it grows older, but such differences are only slight ripples in the basic story.

In later chapters I shall describe the breeding behaviour in more detail. Here it must suffice to say that once the birds have paired and taken possession of a nest site they remain faithful to each other and to their nest for life; though when nest holes are plentiful a pair may have two sites which they use for breeding, sometimes laying in one and sometimes in the other: such sites are usually within a few yards of each other. From one to four broods are raised and as a brood occupies about a month from the laying of the first egg until the fledging of the young it can be seen that pairs which raise three or four broods are pretty fully occupied during the summer months.

When breeding duties are over the adults join the foraging flocks of young birds. Some attachment to the nest site still remains, though it is feeblest at this time of year when flocking occurs and the birds undergo their annual moult. However, many individuals regularly return at night to roost in their nests, even though the remainder of the day is spent away from the breeding area with the flock; this attachment to the nest is usually stronger in males and some at least of them visit their nests every day throughout the year. When the summer flocks begin to break up, the adults return to the breeding areas and now spend much more time at their nests; the juveniles may remain longer in the fields so that when they move to the breeding areas and begin nest-site prospecting the adults are already well established and the young birds are left in no doubt about which holes are already occupied. Sexual and territorial behaviour is still at a rather low ebb and at first the nest owners will tolerate these young birds near their nest. If one of the pair dies towards the end of the breeding season or during the period of autumn flocking, the partner, whether it be the male or female, returns to the nest, remains faithful to it and is usually able to obtain a replacement mate without much delay.

By the end of October there are signs of a recrudescence of sexual behaviour: the adult pairs spend much more time at the nest, nest building is regularly to be seen and parties of nest-site prospecting juveniles will be threatened if they approach too closely to an occupied site. At this time too the adults are frequently to be seen chasing birds of other species, particularly starlings, but also jackdaws and pigeons; presumably much of this behaviour is territorial in origin and the chased bird is being seen off the premises by the owner sparrow, usually the male. One is struck by the easy time that sparrows appear to have, not only in the autumn but at all times of the year apart from the breeding season: they seem to have little difficulty in meeting their requirements—unlike the tits that are always busy combing the trees or the dunnock searching diligently its small chosen patch of ground.

In the late autumn and early winter much time is spent at the nests, but as the days get shorter and the nights colder this becomes less noticeable and a greater proportion of the day is devoted to various social activities: when not at their nests the birds are usually to be found in parties or small flocks of mixed adults and first-year birds, feeding, bathing, singing or just doing nothing together. As the winter gradually passes into spring so the birds' behaviour gradually becomes less social and more time is spent at the nest. At first, nest-site activity is confined to the morning and the pre-roosting period but as the breeding season approaches the pairs may be seen at the nest throughout most of the day.

Nest-site activities may range from one or both of the pair sitting quietly (Plate 4, p. 49) at the nest entrance to nest renovation, sometimes involving the removal of old rubbish from the site, at other times the addition of fresh material. The males spend long periods at the nests calling, and both sexes regularly go inside and stay there for some time. Excitement at the nest sites is most intense when the juveniles are prospecting, both in autumn and in spring.

Just before the start of breeding the intense activity wanes some-what; possibly because the position about ownership has become clarified.

Nest-site activities and social behaviour are inhibited by rain, particularly when continuous. The birds then spend most of the day sheltering; they do not feed much and such food searching as takes place occurs in sheltered places. Outside the breeding season the daily pattern of behaviour is greatly affected by the weather: on mild days the birds spend much more time at their nests than they do when it is cold, though the nearer to the breeding season the less the inhibiting effect of bad weather; however, when there is snow, birds with the entrance to their nests on flat surfaces, for instance under the tiles on a roof, will expend much effort in keeping a clear way in.

In both the areas in which I have watched sparrows, movement of the adults was extremely restricted at all times of the year; it was greatest during the period of flocking to the grain fields, though even this did not amount to much more than a mile or two, and in fact this was the only time when they could not be found in the breeding area throughout the day. I used to see many of my colour-ringed birds every day of their lives except when I was away from home. On the other hand, in less highly populated country districts the birds appear to be slightly more mobile and, in the winter, the breeding colonies may be deserted during the day, the birds being found foraging some distance away frequently with flocks of finches and buntings.

The general pattern was more or less the same in both my study areas and is probably typical of the bird throughout most of its range, though slight modifications no doubt occur: thus summer flocking is probably not as pronounced among birds living in the centres of large towns; in exposed places, nesting areas may be evacuated in the winter months. Some differences are, however, evident from a study of house sparrows at Cornell University by R. L. Weaver. He found that a wintering flock numbering about six thousand birds was formed in the area of some barns where the breeding-season population was only about thirty pairs, the remainder of the winter flock dispersing over an area of about two miles radius to breed in farms and the nearby town of Ithaca. Weaver suggests that this behaviour may have resulted from the combined circumstances of a plentiful supply of food and a shortage of nesting sites (although additional sites were provided by putting up nest-boxes); this is supported by the observation that the same nesting sites were used by different pairs in succession. On the other hand, he states that many sites were not used at all. I would suggest that the breeding population was determined rather by the supply of food available for rearing the young. As we shall see in a later chapter, house sparrows will build in a great variety of sites, including trees and bushes; so I feel that it is unlikely that breeding population could be controlled by a shortage of sites. The pattern of behaviour observed by Weaver does not appear to be typical for the United States; however, the observations are interesting in showing how differences from the normal pattern occur as an adaptation to meet local circumstances.

A much greater difference exists in part of the bird's range in Asia, where it is a true migrant, rearing only one brood and being absent from October to May (see Chapter 11). In general, however, the species is characterised by the combination of the importance of its nest site throughout the year, its sedentary habits and its social behaviour. Now let us look more closely at some of these activities that go to make up the daily pattern of existence, rather than the broader seasonal pattern we have been considering in these last two chapters.

CHAPTER 4

EVERYDAY LIFE

MOST IMPORTANT in daily activities are feeding behaviour and, in a social species, communication between individuals; in all species, in addition, beyond the routine of day-to-day living, some form of communication between the pair is necessary for successful breeding. All of the five senses are used by animals in communication, but only two are of importance where the majority of birds are concerned—sight and sound. The behaviour having the function of communication is instinctive or innate; reasoning processes are absent and all individuals of the species react to the same situation with the same postures and calls. These are in fact an overt expression of the emotions which we label as hunger, fear, anger and sex, and, although they cannot be thought of as an elementary form of language, they function as a signal system between individuals and indeed as such have, as a result of evolution, become more conspicuous and specific, the postures frequently being associated with particular plumage patterns and calls.

N. Tinbergen, particularly from studies of the three-spined stickleback and the herring gull, has shown how instinctive behaviour depends both on internal and external motivating factors: hunger and sexual development are typical internal factors, other birds of the same species, predators, the nest, being typical external ones. Thus territorial and sexual behaviour depend not only on the presence of a nest or of a bird of the opposite sex but also upon the existence of a certain internal state. We have seen in the previous chapter how first-year prospecting birds are at first tolerated by the nest owner, but in a few weeks are driven away; developments in the internal sexual cycle of the males occur during this period (possibly governed by an internal rhythm) and provide the necessary internal part of the stimulus that combines with the external stimulus of a rival at the nest and triggers off or releases territorial behaviour. Tinbergen then goes on to suggest a hierarchical organisation controlling activities at different levels, each level requiring a certain degree of stimulus before the activity it controls is released, successive levels becoming more and more specific in their reaction to the stimuli so that the ultimate behaviour pattern is appropriate to the situation. This means that only one of the available instinctive activities is possible at one time; however, where there are two different stimuli or releasers of almost equal intensity both of the natural activities are thwarted and the build up of stimulus potential is dissipated by some apparently incongruous activity that appears to be out-of-context. This incongruous behaviour is termed a displacement activity and Tinbergen has shown that such displacement activities have secondarily evolved as signals in their own right, becoming ritualised in the process so that it is often difficult to recognise the original source of the behaviour.

Tinbergen's analysis of instinct has given a new direction to the detailed study of behaviour, whereby a complex activity can be broken down into its constituent parts and a deeper insight obtained of the whole sequence of events. It is against this background that I shall attempt to describe the components of the house sparrow's behaviour, though I must freely admit that many of the interpretations are no more than tentative, while in other cases I can merely describe the behaviour without offering even a tentative interpretation; this is a necessary consequence of my failure to subject the birds to experimental situations, an essential factor in unravelling the details of the behaviour patterns. However, it is possible even with a purely observational approach to identify the underlying significance of the basic postures, a knowledge of which is of great value in attempting to interpret some of the more complex behaviour situations.

The basic emotional states that we can hope to understand by observing the birds are those involving fear, aggression (anger) and sex. For simplicity of description I shall separate the posturings and calls used by the house sparrow, although this is of course quite artificial because many of the postures have particular calls associated with them and it is the combination of movement and sound that go together to complete the picture.

A frequent movement seen in house sparrows is a sharp flicking of the tail. A "strange" male investigating a nest site regularly flicks his tail; a bird at a nest with food for the young but not going in because of the presence of an observer, or even one away from the nest when approached by man or some other enemy, behaves

FIG. 1. Cock tail flicking: based on two successive shots from cine film.

in a similar way. This behaviour is clearly an indication of fear or nervousness. A bird that is afraid is ready for immediate flight and shows this by sleeking the plumage and raising the tail (a flight-intention movement). It is tempting to think that tail flicking is a signal that has evolved from the simple movement of tail raising prior to flight, but Fig. 1, above, which is drawn from two successive frames of a cine-film, shows that the movement is actually a depressing of the tail. Its value in territorial situations is that it shows other sparrows that the bird is not aggressively motivated and thus by putting itself in a subordinate position it helps to prevent unnecessary attacks and relieves the individual of the need to fly away from another sparrow as soon as it becomes afraid. In a social situation it helps to warn other birds of possible danger when this is still at a low level. Further evidence supporting this interpretation is shown by the evident appearance of nervousness in the bird that is flicking its tail.

FIG. 2. Hen in threat posture.

A bird that is preparing for attack thrusts its head forward; this is an indication of threat or aggression. In a more intense state of emotion the wings are held slightly out from the body and may be flicked upwards; the bill may be gaped (Fig. 2, above). The same threat posture is used by both sexes, the bird facing directly towards its opponent: in the male the black and white plumage of the head presents a striking pattern when viewed directly from the front; in addition the wings may be slightly rotated enhancing the effect by showing off the white wing bars (Fig. 3, opposite). Gaping is more particularly adopted by the female—no doubt to make up for her less striking plumage. When threatening the feathers are also sleeked and the bird is prepared for flight, this time towards rather than away from its opponent. This threat posture is used against a trespasser near the nest, during feeding when another

bird tries to steal the food or during dust bathing when another
bird approaches too closely the dust-bathing hollow. The posture
itself is frequently sufficient to deter the other bird and is thus of
value to the species as it prevents unnecessary fighting. When the
posture is not sufficient to deter the rival the bird may go over
into attack—it lunges forward with its open bill and attempts to

FIG. 3. Cock in intense threat posture.

seize its opponent's nape, wings or tail. On the rare occasion that
this fails to drive off the other bird a fight may ensue. Now the two
birds peck at each other and may flutter up in the air, breast to
breast, still pecking away; if perched above the ground they may
lose balance and fall down clasping each other's bill or one bird
holding on to the other's plumage. In fighting the aim appears to
be to force the other bird on to its back on the ground, where it is
held with the feet and stabbed viciously with the bill; on rare
occasions one bird may even kill another in this way.

Lunging and gaping are a part of real fighting; the flicking of
the wings, which is enhanced by the plumage pattern in the male,
has evolved as part of the threat posture, making this quite specific
and thus eliminating fighting in all but a few cases when the
threatened bird stands its ground; similar wing-flicking movements
that are used in water and dust bathing may be homologous.

In another posture used in quite a different group of situations,
the bird crouches with the neck drawn in and the wings slightly
drooped and shivered. This attitude is in fact quite the opposite to
the one used in threat. It is first seen in the young birds when

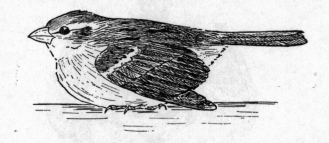

FIG. 4. Hen in solicitation posture.

begging food from their parents (Plate 5, p. 64) and this is probably
the origin of the behaviour; it is used by the unmated male with a
nest trying to attract a female and by a female inviting her mate to
coition (Fig. 4, above). In these contexts it is clearly an invitation
or solicitation attitude. It is also used by the male when his young
are almost ready to fledge; now the male's rate of bringing food to
the young decreases markedly and he spends much time near the
nest in the wing-shivering attitude (Fig. 5, opposite). It seems that
he is attempting to attract the young away from the nest; again the
function is invitation, though it is more difficult to understand how
the behaviour can have evolved in this context. Possibly internal
factors play some part—the parental drive waning and the sexual
drive assuming dominance over it; that is, the behaviour may have
originated as an invitation to the female, though it now appears to
be directed as much towards the young. This interpretation is

supported by the fact that there is nothing comparable in the hen. I have also seen a young bird adopt a submissive crouched posture and shiver its wings when attacked by another bird; here the behaviour appears to be used submissively to inhibit aggression.

Fighting in a territorial context takes place only between birds of the same sex. When a female appears near the nest of a sexually

FIG. 5. Cock in solicitation posture.

active male, he displays to her by strutting in front of her in what I call the "standing to attention" posture (Fig. 6, p. 24)—the bird seems unnaturally stiff and takes on rather a military appearance. In this posture the head is held up with the chest thrust forward showing off the black bib, which contrasts with the grey cheeks and underparts; the wings are held out slightly from the body and pressed downwards (sometimes even trailing on the ground) with the upper surfaces slightly forward so that the white wing bar is obvious; the tail is elevated and fanned, drawing attention to the grey back and rump, which have been exposed by the drooped wings and which contrast with the darker wings and tail; the rump feathers are further accentuated by being fluffed up. In the display posture the male hops round in front of the female and may bow stiffly up and down; it should be noted that he does not face directly towards her and the wings are not flicked as in the threat

FIG. 6. Cock in sexual display posture.

posture. The hen that is not ready for the male responds by adopting the threat posture previously described and the male is subject to the two opposing drives of sex and fear (the female appears to assume a position of dominance over the male at this stage of the sexual cycle), which has given rise to a displacement activity that has now evolved as a sexual display with the function of stimulating the sexual development of the female.

Bill wiping is another activity that seems to have a special significance; it appears more frequently than is occasioned by the necessity for cleaning after feeding. In some situations it appears to be used when the bird is afraid—a bird that is disturbed from the ground flies up to a tree or other high perch and there wipes its bill—between mountings of the hen the cock also frequently wipes its bill. It is probably a displacement activity but further study is necessary before a complete interpretation of its significance can be attempted.

It will be seen how the bird's plumage pattern has evolved with these postures. Not only do the white wing bars, the black throat and the grey rump enhance the effect but they become more conspicuous as the breeding season approaches—after the moult the male's plumage is less striking, but with the gradual abrasion of the feather tips during the winter months the various features become more noticeable—when display and territorial threat are most important in the bird's life.

Although it is convenient to separate voice from the above posturings for the sake of simplicity of description, this is of course quite artificial because many of these postures have particular calls associated with them and it is the combination of movement and sound that go together to complete the picture. It is very difficult to create an impression of bird sounds, apart from a few stereotyped songs with a pronounced rhythm like the well known "little bit of bread and no cheese" of the yellowhammer, as so many of these are quite different from those used by man and can only inadequately be represented verbally. The same call may be portrayed by two observers with a very different series of vowels and consonants, together with accents and epithets such as nasal, harsh, etc., in an attempt to creat a more faithful impression. There are two reasons for this: one is subjective—there is no doubt that the same call sounds differently to the same observer at different times, as can be readily proved to oneself by listening to a recording of a bird call, translating it into a verbal form and then repeating the process some time later, when the original transcription has been forgotten; on the other hand, there is no doubt that the calls themselves can be very variable—not only is there variation between individuals but also in the same individual on different occasions. The significance of bird calls is intimately bound up with time, place and manner of delivery.

With this apologia I should now like to attempt to describe the various calls used by the house sparrow. For each call I give a number of verbal representations that have appealed to me from time to time: in addition, I shall describe some typical circumstances in which each of the calls is used and attempt to associate some significance or emotional state with them. The voice of the house sparrow has already been discussed by A. Daanje; where possible his representation of the calls is identified with mine (the German pronunciation of his representations should be borne in mind) and his assessment of the significance compared with my own.

The main and most widely used call is the "chirrup" that gives the bird his name Philip Sparrow—"all sparrows are called Philip, 'phip phip!' they cry". This call may be quite variable—it may be shortened to the monosyllabic "chirp", "chweep", "cheep" or "cheerp", while the disyllabic version may at times sound like "chirrip", "cheerup", "chee-up" or "chillip". All these representations have the common initial "ch" and the final hard "p". (Daanje's versions are "schielp" or "pielp".) This variability may in part be the result of differences between individuals and could be a useful factor in recognition; this is of particular importance in a social species and might account for some of the variety in the house sparrow's chirrup calls.

This call is used in a variety of circumstances, but the common thread seems to be one of the bird proclaiming its identity—"I am a House Sparrow!" For example, it is used by the male to proclaim his ownership of a nest site in what may be termed "advertisement calling". This can be heard at almost all times of the year except possibly towards the end of the summer. Males that have completed their moult by the end of September start calling from beside their nests; it becomes more noticeable in October and persists throughout the winter, more and more time being spent in this activity as the breeding season approaches. Used in this context the call is not associated with any particular form of display; it is not delivered very excitedly and may be soft and intermittent or louder and uttered at a rate of about one call every two seconds to two every three seconds. However, when the bird is attempting to attract a mate, the manner in which the call is given is quite different—the rate is speeded up to more than one call a second, sometimes even two calls a second, and the notes tend to be higher pitched ("chirrip" or "cheep" rather than "chirrup") and more excited; a rhythm may be introduced into the sequence of calls ("cheep chirrip chirrip" or "chirrip cheep chirrip") with the groups lasting about one second and separated by about three seconds, or in long bursts of chirrups lasting for up to ten seconds. The male seeking a mate in April or May will spend a major proportion of the day at his nest calling in this way; the longer he is without a mate the more excited and continuous his calling becomes and at times it is associated with wing shivering, especially when a hen appears nearby.

One first-year cock in 1953, who actually failed to obtain a mate that year, called at his nest in this way from the beginning of March until the end of July. From the end of March until the middle of June he called regularly every day from beside the nest, and during this time had frequent bursts of ecstatic calling and wing shivering. The nest was situated at the gable end of a cottage just underneath where the gutter ended. His advertisement calling and some of the more excited calling was given from the gutter immediately above the nest but, as he continued to be unsuccessful in attracting a hen, he changed his song post to the top of the gable end, where he called and displayed in a most conspicuous way.

Another cock gave the advertisement call regularly on a gutter from July 1952 until June 1953. He also failed to obtain a mate and, in fact, where he was calling there was no suitable hole available for use as a nest site. He never used the excited mate-seeking calling, though from time to time he took part in the communal sexual displays. This bird must have been abnormal in some way, as a cock with a nest site will regularly visit it and even build a nest although he fails to obtain a mate. The male also uses the ecstatic form of the call in the sexual displays that are described more fully in Chapter 7.

Away from the nest and unconnected with sexual activities chirrup calls are frequently used, particularly from cocks that have just left the roost in the morning but also at any time of the day in hedges and trees away from nests. In these circumstances it is less incisive and uttered more slowly than in advertisement calling; soft "chweeps" and "chirrups" are the most usual variants heard and at times these may be strung together to form a rudimentary song, e.g. "chirrup-tee-chirrup-chirp-chirp" and "chirri-pip-pip". This whole performance suggests a feeling of contentment—well-being after emerging from a peaceful night's sleep or the satisfaction of being well fed, having nothing to do and not being in danger. A sweeter type of song that is occasionally heard from juveniles I shall refer to in a later chapter. Regularly outside the breeding season, especially when normal activities at nest sites are inhibited by wet weather or fog, or in the winter afternoons when such activities are in any case less frequent, a number of birds of both sexes will collect together in close cover, such as ivy, holly or a cypress, or in the higher branches of a tree, and indulge in what may be termed social song. Chirrup notes are used and the whole performance gives the impression of being conversational. Here is a typical example heard on the afternoon of 11th March, 1951, when it was damp and foggy. About twenty to thirty sparrows were gathered in a dense, ivy-clad holly tree at about 2.30 p.m. These birds were chirruping continuously like a flock going to roost. There was little excited activity and both sexes were present. At times the calling would cease and there would be complete silence for a few seconds till one bird started and the chorus would begin anew. Even with a dog barking underneath (at the noise of the birds) the song continued undisturbed. Half an hour later the din was still going on.

Again, on several occasions when I have disturbed some birds from a favoured feeding place, such as a hen-run, they have collected in trees above out of sight and indulged in social song. It is perhaps relevant that here also the birds have been inhibited from another activity. This, as the name I have used is intended to convey, is very much a social activity; like solitary calling it seems to be a way of passing the time when there is nothing more pressing requiring attention. House sparrows appear to have plenty of spare time outside the breeding season; this singing seems to be one way of maintaining the strong social bond of the colony. It regularly occurs as a prelude to roosting, especially when a communal roost is being used, and at times hundreds of birds may take part.

This omnibus call is used in yet a further variety of situations, again with the function of drawing attention: the cock uses it, in the more excited version with the wing-shivering enticement display, to attract the young from the nest when they are almost ready to fledge; in fact, during the last two or three days before fledging the male may almost give up feeding the young and spend most of his time near the nest calling and displaying in this way. Young birds begging food from their parents adopt almost the same attitude though the call tends to be somewhat thinner, more sibilant and shriller (Daanje: "schiep-schiep-schiep"); this calling rises to a crescendo each time one of the adults arrives at the nest with food.

Although basically this call belongs to the cock, it is also used by the hen: she joins in with chirrups during social singing and sometimes she will call at the nest at the beginning of the breeding season, particularly if she has lost her mate. In general, the chirrup uttered by the hen is much softer than that of the cock.

Finally the flight call used by both sexes belongs to this group of calls. I think it can best be conveyed by "churrip" (though I have frequently represented it in my notes by "churrit" and "turrip" as well); it differs from the other chirrup calls in that the second syllable is accentuated rather than the first and it is also softer and lower-pitched.

Next we come to the calls used between a mated pair; these are almost invariably connected with the nest and breeding, and can be described as appeasement calls, being used to inhibit the aggressive behaviour that is liable to arise when two birds are forced into close contact with each other. These calls are used by both sexes and are very variable; they have the common characteristic of a long "ee" sound, are rather soft and are usually uttered rather urgently in groups of two to five notes or in a continuous flow. I think the best representation is "quee", but at times I have used the following: "chee", "tchee", "dee", "pee", "queh" and even "cheep", though this last version is quite distinguishable from the "cheep" variant of the chirrup call.

When the hen adopts the "solicitation" posture to invite the cock to coition, she commonly calls a continuous "quee-quee-quee-quee" as she is shivering her wings. Sometimes the cock uses the same call during his run up to mount. G. Beven, who considers that the calling in this situation is more commonly attributable to the cock, describes it as "tee-tee-tee": I have frequently found it difficult to distinguish which of the birds is calling. The sight, or sound, of a pair mating often stimulates other pairs at nearby nests to the same activity.

A very similar call is used in change-over ceremonies at the nest, the relieving bird calling a group of "quee" notes as it arrives and often simultaneously giving a few wing-shivers; on this the mate comes out of the nest and the change-over takes place. In a similar way the bird bringing food to the nest may pause and call "quee" before going in. In this context it is very clearly an appeasement call as it is used much more frequently at the beginning of the breeding season before the birds have got really used to each other; later by far the greatest number of arrivals at the nest during incubation or after the young have hatched are unheralded by calling or display. In a species in which the birds mate for life and are regularly together it is probable that elaborate ceremonies at the nest are not needed; presentation of nest material and feeding of the hen by the cock do occur but they are rather infrequent.

Daanje terms this call the "infantile (solicitation) call" ("die die die") and is of the opinion that it is the same as the first call used by the nestlings, which is retained by the adults. He considers it to be an invitation to the partner in pairing or nest relief. He says that both adults use the same call to get the fledglings to follow them, though I have not noticed this, and suggests that it is akin to baby language in humans.

Another call frequently to be heard at the nest during the breeding season I term the "churr"; at times it sounds like "churr-r-r-it-it-it-it", at others it is more like "chit-it-it-it-it" or an intermediate "chur-tit-tit-tit-tit" (Daanje: "terrettettet"). This is uttered by the hen when she arrives at the nest and may be a prelude to the solicitation calls and behaviour that precede coition. Later in the breeding cycle, it is used when the hen is impatient to take the cock's place in the nest; again it may be succeeded by solicitation if the cock does not come out. I believe that this is an assertive or threat call, used during the period of breeding when the hen assumes dominancy over the cock; at times she also uses it as a threat in the communal display (see Chapter 7).

The "churr" is used by the cock against intruders at the nest, both against other male sparrows and against other species, particularly starlings, which regularly look into sparrow holes, but I have also heard it used against a mistle thrush stealing grass from an open house sparrow nest in a tree. In this context the threat aspect is more obvious and when the intruder flies off it is usually chased by the owner sparrow. It is never, in my experience, used by the male towards his mate, though she will use it against him when she is not ready for coition and against other males displaying to her. It is also frequently heard from the innermost recesses of a communal roost, but here it is not possible to say which of the sexes is responsible. The contrast of this situation to the friendly spirit that exists during social singing should be noted; disputes over favoured roosting perches are obviously frequent. Further it may be associated with the aggressive postures that take place over food and dust-bathing sites. Daanje concludes from his observations that the "churr" is not an expression of a simple flight or attack mood but is rather more complex; he describes it as a "nervous reaction" and indeed it is somewhat difficult to separate the emotions of fear and threat in many of these situations.

The alarm call has a distinctly nasal timbre about it and most frequently sounds to me like "quer", a single note or repeated two or three times "quer-quer-quer"—variants "cher cher", "quer-it", "quer-ik", "ki-quer" and "ki-quer-kit"; (Daanje: "kew kew"). It appears to be used most often in ambivalent situations; namely, it is used when the bird's instinct is to fly away to avoid danger but it is inhibited in this by wanting to feed or protect the young, that is, it is a displacement reaction. For example, it is used by an adult at the nest with food but reluctant to enter because of the presence of a human being or cat, when a cock calling and displaying to attract the young from the nest sees a predator, such as a crow or cat, and by an adult when one of its newly fledged young has been trapped and is being handled. When used by an adult with young in the nest it immediately silences the young, who normally chirp loudly when their parents are near. In the same way when one member of a feeding flock uses this call the remainder fly to the safety of a hedge; in this situation the ambivalence is between feeding and escape. The calling of the alarm "quer" is frequently associated with tail flicking, which we have seen is an expression of fear or nervousness; for example, a male stealing nesting material from a tree nest calls "quer" and flicks his tail. The "quer quer" notes and variants are frequently heard in the communal roost before the birds settle for the night.

When a bird has been trapped it will use the "quer quer" call on being approached; sometimes, however, on being handled this is changed to a shrill "chree". I think this is a fear or extreme alarm call; Daanje, whose version is "kruu", considers that the two alarm calls are used in different situations; the "kew kew" on the appearance of an enemy from which the bird can escape by taking flight, e.g. man or cat; the "kruu" for an enemy which can attack it in the air, e.g. a sparrow-hawk. The reaction of other sparrows to the second call is to take cover or to remain still and silent—food-seeking birds remain sitting quite motionless, cocks stop chirping at their nests and even displays and coition are broken off; whereas the former call may attract others to join the calling bird against the enemy, for example, in "mobbing" a cat. My experience on the reaction of sparrows to birds of prey is rather limited, though I have seen sparrows call "chree" at a flying kestrel.

As intercommunication by visual and auditory signals is perforce part of everyday life, so is feeding. Much is known about the food taken by the house sparrow as a result of numerous examinations of stomach contents that have been made in different parts of the bird's range. This species is very catholic in its choice of food and with such a wide distribution many different types of vegetable food and species of insects are taken; it would be tedious to attempt to give a complete list—E. R. Kalmbach in America was able to

PLATE I. Male house sparrow. (*J. Markham*)

PLATE 2. Female house sparrow. (*E. Hosking*)

identify 838 specifically different items of food in 8,004 stomachs examined. However it is worth examining the more important of the foodstuffs eaten. The sparrows,* as shown by their broad thick bills, are primarily seed eaters, with the house sparrow a specialist in grain. Animal food is particularly important in the diet of the nestlings, though it is also taken to a certain extent all through the bird's life. The proportion of the various types of food depends both on the time of year and particularly the habitat: rural birds have more access to grain than urban ones, more especially now that the horse has been displaced from towns with the loss to the sparrows of the chaff from the nosebags and undigested remains from the droppings, and also more opportunity of stealing food put out for hens and pigs; urban-living birds now specialise on "artificial foods" such as bread, fat and other scraps that are always to be found near houses. Seeds of weeds and grasses are taken whenever available and, though less important, tree seeds, fruit and green vegetable matter.

The type of grain depends of course on its availability and oats, wheat, rye, barley, corn, sorghum, millet and rice have all been recorded. The bird does, however, appear to have definite preferences and where a variety of cereals are grown, oats and wheat are taken first. Although grain is most important during the time of harvest when the birds visit the ripening crops, it has been found in sparrows' stomachs at all times of year; much of this must come from spillage and waste or from feed intended for domestic animals.

Among the weed seeds taken the most important are grasses (*Gramineae*) and rushes (*Juncaceae*), goosefoot (*Chenopodium alba*), docks (particularly knotgrass, *Polygonum aviculare*) and chickweeds (*Stellaria media* and *Cerastium* sp.). The tree seeds most frequently eaten are those of birch (*Betula*) and elm (*Ulmus*), but like fruits, of which grapes and cherries are mentioned most often in the literature, these do not form a really significant item of food except possibly in rather unusual circumstances. Although seeds form the major part of vegetable food taken by the bird, it also very regularly

* I refer here to the old-world sparrows of the genus *Passer;* the so-called sparrows of North America belong to the family Emberizidae and are not related.

takes the leaves of dandelion, clover and nettle, the fresh green shoots of peas, lettuce and other vegetables and also buds from practically every known type of fruit tree and bush.

The animal foods principally taken are insects and members of over half of the twenty-four orders have been recorded. The most important types, however, are: beetles (*Coleoptera*), particularly weevils and dung beetles; bugs (*Hemiptera*), mainly aphides (*Aphididae*) and scale-insects (*Coccidae*); flies (*Diptera*), both craneflies (*Tipulidae*) and muscid flies (*Muscidae*), particularly the house fly in all its forms—larva, pupa and adult; moths (*Lepidoptera*), mostly as caterpillars though also a few adults, and grasshoppers (*Orthoptera*). Other animal food taken includes earthworms, spiders, snails, millipedes, young frogs and, of course, scrap meat fibres and fat.

The choice of animal food is probably determined mostly by availability—sparrows living near the sea will take molluscs and crustaceans from the shore—and numerous reports stress how quick the sparrow is to exploit any abnormal abundance of insects. Much of this animal food is given to the nestlings but adults collecting for their young frequently eat a considerable amount of the same food themselves, whereas adults without young take a preponderance of vegetable food, though I have regularly seen sparrows feeding on blackfly in the autumn after the breeding season.

The difference between the diet of adults and nestlings is strikingly shown in Table 1, which is due to E. R. Kalmbach and is based on stomach analyses of birds collected from all parts of the United States. By analysing birds collected from different areas separately, Kalmbach found the proportion of vegetable food in the nestlings to range from seven to forty-three per cent, the highest coming from an urban environment; almost half of the food of these urban sparrows consisted of caterpillars. From my observations I should think that bread might well account for more than fifty per cent of the food given to nestlings in suburban districts.

It will be seen that most of the insects and other animals taken are slow moving, though some more mobile prey is also taken; it

TABLE I

Food Items from House Sparrows expressed as
Volume Percentages (Kalmbach)

	Weevils	Other beetles	Grass-hoppers	Cater-pillars	Other insects	Spiders etc.	Grain
Adults (2,931 birds)	1·45	2·92	1·20	0·50	0·84	0·12	92·97
Nestlings (2,819 birds)	15·17	8·84	25·24	11·16	5·72	2·00	31·87

is of interest to see how this animal food is obtained by a bird
primarily adapted to living on vegetable food. Several techniques
are used and are most noticeable when the birds are feeding young
in the nest, though the adults also collect insect food for themselves
when it is readily available.

Flycatching is the most conspicuous of the methods, though one
of the least successful. I have seen house sparrows behaving like
flycatchers from February to May and again from July to September; presumably it occurs at any time of the year when insects can
be got in this way, though I think it is a spare time activity and is
not as frequently used a method of collecting food for the young as
some of the others. It is often seen when ants are swarming, sparrows
joining the starlings, chaffinches and other species that are also
taking part. The sparrows may operate from a perch or from the
ground and appear particularly clumsy on the wing compared
with spotted flycatchers and other aerial feeders. At times they also
chase moths and I have seen one bird keeping up a chase for over
five minutes, landing when the moth was lost to sight and giving
chase when it was located again; at the end of five minutes the
moth disappeared from sight with the sparrow still after it. Cockchafers are also taken in flight; these beetles do not normally fly
by day and those that do have presumably been disturbed and
being rather clumsy flyers are readily caught. The insect is then
taken to some hard surface and beaten to death. My aviary birds

also killed the maggots I supplied by striking them against the ground before feeding them to their young.

Hovering and pouncing is used when the sparrow is collecting insects from long grass or rushes. The birds fly low over the clumps of grass and hover a few inches above the vegetation with tail depressed and fanned, legs dangling like a miniature kestrel; when an insect is seen the bird drops on it. The birds near my rural study colony frequently obtained insects in this way from a patch of rushes in a marshy field about a hundred yards away from the nesting sites. Individual birds appeared to be able to collect sufficient food by this technique in five minutes to justify a return trip to the nest. Sparrows also use a pouncing technique when obtaining insects from bare earth; they fly rapidly over the ground about a foot up with rapid changes of direction and when an insect is located the bird quickly wheels round and drops on it. This is presumably a more efficient way of searching bare ground than hopping over it. Birds will also hover in front of sunny brick walls and fly up and take insects settled there without landing.

More methodical searching is employed with slow-moving insects, in trees and bushes and on the trunks of trees. The bird searches the undersides of leaves and picks off the prey. I have watched a bird collecting greenfly in this way from a rose bush only a few yards from the nest and feeding her young on little else. This bird lost her mate after the young were about three days old and successfully reared the young by herself on this readily available supply of food. Blackfly are also regularly taken in this way from apple trees in October and November and presumably many of the small caterpillars that are fed to the young in the nest are obtained like this. Flies and other insects are also searched for in porches and under eaves where they are caught in cobwebs and under glass roofs in railway stations where they appear to get trapped. Newly emerging dragonflies are taken before they are able to fly.

Active searching is used to obtain faster-moving prey, both in bushes and among grass. It is a combination of the techniques used in hovering and pouncing and methodical searching—as soon as the insect is located it is seized by a sudden pounce.

Evidence of the adaptability of the house sparrow is shown by records of birds feeding their young long after dark by catching moths and other insects attracted to electric lights and neon signs—if the moths were dazzled, the sparrows certainly were not! Another interesting piece of opportunism is the way sparrows take from parked cars the dead insects trapped in the radiator grilles; this has been recorded in England, America and Australia.

Thus while the house sparrow is not a specialised insect feeder it has become sufficiently adept in the food-collecting techniques of such diverse species as flycatchers, warblers and tits (leaf searching) and tree creepers (bark searching) to be able to feed its young on insects and augment its own diet with substantial amounts of animal food.

Some other rather unusual feeding techniques are worthy of mention. Two instances have been recorded of house sparrows softening hard crusts of bread in water; in both cases the birds brought the bread to the water and either dipped it in or allowed it to float until it could be readily broken up. It would appear that this behaviour may have arisen from the accidental discovery by individual birds that water would soften bread, probably in the same way that tits acquired the habit of opening milk-bottles: both these are probably examples of random exploratory behaviour leading to the learning of new methods of obtaining food. House sparrows have been recorded drinking milk from bottles; this has presumably been copied from tits, with which the behaviour originated, but the habit has been learned as a number of cases have been reported in which the sparrows were seen to open the milk bottles themselves. Another habit, tit-like in action and certainly individually acquired by sparrows, is the use of the foot to hold food, particularly hard bread, so that it can be broken up and eaten; I have seen this only once, but it has been reported in the literature and was acquired by Mrs. Kipps's Clarence late on in his life. This remarkable bird also began to walk instead of hopping as his physical powers failed, a feat I have only once heard of in a wild house sparrow and then only for a few steps.

Another thing that is frequently eaten is grit, including small stones, sand, brick, etc.; this may be used as an aid to digestion, and few sparrows are dissected without some pieces of stone being found in their gizzards, but in addition egg shells and mortar are so regularly taken that they appear to form an essential part of the bird's diet. This may be connected with bone-building as it is found in the young, though whether eaten deliberately or taken accidentally with other foods cannot be said with certainty. Finally house sparrows have been reported pecking at a salt lick put out for cattle in Indiana, U.S.A.

The habit of tearing flowers is a puzzling one and though many people have commented on it a satisfactory explanation is still lacking. The behaviour is most frequent in the spring in March and April; it also occurs in autumn but much less commonly. Yellow is the colour most often attacked and I have watched the birds select yellow crocuses out of a bed containing white and purple flowers as well. Again in a mixed bed of yellow and yellow-red variegated polyanthus, the yellow ones may be attacked but the variegated left alone. Other yellow flowers that I have seen despoiled are: lesser celandine, primrose, primula and dandelion. Despite reports that other colours of flowers are attacked, for example the purple wanda primula (in December and March), the selection of yellow from a mixed bed does suggest a definite preference for this colour, though it is perhaps not without relevance that yellow is the predominant flower colour in the spring in Britain. All of the plants mentioned above are small with the flower heads readily accessible to a sparrow on the ground. If the flower is examined closely after it has been attacked it will be seen that this has not been purely random but that the petals are carefully torn into shreds and I suspect that at least part of them is eaten; E. R. Kalmbach in his study of the feeding behaviour of house sparrows in America reported flower petals from their stomachs. Another feature that has been remarked is that the habit is most prevalent in dry seasons, though this is more of an impression and has not, as far as I know, been tested by careful observation. This suggests that the birds may be getting something from the petals and that it is not just wanton damage. Flower tearing is probably analogous to the eating of vegetable matter, such as buds, young vegetables and various leaves. One observer noticed in the dry spring of 1922 that sparrows were snipping off the juicy flower shoots of clove plants but that when he put out a dish of water they desisted. I have numerous records of bud and leaf eating; with very few exceptions these are all in the period January to April. I feel that flower tearing is definitely associated with feeding but that it is to a certain extent a spare time activity—during the spring months the sparrows have lots of spare time and this is one of the ways in which it is used; in the breeding season, time is at a premium, and at other times of the year the need for vegetable food is satisfied by all sorts of seeds from weeds to grasses, rushes, cereals and even trees. Fruits are often attacked in a sporadic sort of way that suggests a temporary shortage of moisture. The predilection for yellow has probably arisen from the fact that this is the commonest colour of wild flowers during the months when flower tearing is practised.

The selection of yellow flowers shows a certain power of colour discrimination. J. P. Porter, who carried out experiments in America on house sparrows in an aviary, found that they could distinguish blue, green, yellow, red, light and dark grey, though there was apparently some confusion between yellow and red. I have put out dyed rice (in addition to white, the colours used were blue, green, yellow, orange and pink) for both wild and captive birds; the order in which the different colours were taken was not the same in all of the tests, but the overall order of preference was as follows: blue, green, white, yellow, orange and pink. Blue food is a surprising choice; it is interesting though that the colours are chosen in spectral order with the red end, where Porter found some lack of discrimination, least popular. Experiments with other diurnal birds have shown that discrimination is normally better at the red than at the blue end, contrary to the above observations; red discrimination is most useful in the early morning and late evening light—perhaps it is not so necessary in the late-rising and early-retiring sparrow! Brown is also recognised; during nest building the birds fly down to a brown patch on a lawn to get the dead grass they prefer for the structure of the nest. At a later stage white feathers are chosen in preference to coloured ones for nest lining; possibly they make the chicks easier to see in the darkness of the nest cavity.

For all their low-living ways house sparrows are great exponents of toilet behaviour—water-bathing (Plate 6a, p. 65), dust-bathing (Plate 6b, p. 65), and preening; perhaps this is associated with the bird continuing to use the same nest, not only for breeding but also throughout the year for roosting, and this may expose the birds to excessive risks of infestation by nest-living parasites. Water and dust-bathing, like so much of the sparrow's behaviour, are usually communal activities, numbers of the birds performing together—two hundred have been seen dust-bathing together in Egypt.

Gilbert White observed that: "House Sparrows are great *pulveratrices*, being frequently seen grovelling and wallowing in dusty roads." Dust-bathing is most often seen in the sandy soil of flower and vegetable beds during dry weather and frequently such places get quite pock-marked with the small craters that the birds hollow out. When a party of birds is dusting together, disputes are frequent as the birds in their excessive energy and enthusiasm encroach on the dusting sites of their neighbours. On landing at the chosen spot, the bird bends its legs and leans forward on its chest; the soil may be thrown up with the closed bill, flicked up with the wings or the wings may be extended and shuffled in the soft soil and then brought up full of dust which lands among the fluffed-up body feathers. The bird shuffles round while doing this so that a crater is hollowed out and at times the feet are used to kick the dirt away backwards. K. E. L. Simmons, who has described the process in some detail, remarks that the movements are the same as those used in water-bathing. The birds bathe in water at all times of the year—I have even seen them bathing in melting snow—and regularly afterwards they seek out some dry sandy soil to follow up with a dust-bath. Both types of bath are usually followed by preening, the bird carefully drawing the primaries and tail feathers through the bill.

Although sparrows sometimes sun-bathe in their dust-bathing craters, this is more frequently done in the safety of a roof-top; again sun-bathing may be seen at any time of the year—even in the middle of winter if the bird can find a sheltered spot in the sun behind a chimney. In the sun-bathing posture the bird lies flat on its belly with the wings slightly held out or even fully extended and laid flat on the tiles, the body feathers fluffed out. I have seen birds lying in this blissful state for over thirty minutes.

In the foregoing pages I have tried to give a general picture of the house sparrow's daily life. Now, against this broad pattern, I should like to deal more particularly with some specialised aspects; the first of these, and the most important, is breeding, which I shall discuss in the next few chapters.

CHAPTER 5

PAIR FORMATION

As WE have seen, the nest is a most important factor in the life of the house sparrow; one or both of the owners usually roost in it and both are frequently to be seen at it during the day at all times of the year. A remarkable instance of the strength of this attachment to the nest is given by R. Meinertzhagen; he records that a number of pairs of house sparrows had built in the sails of a house-boat on the Nile and that these birds accompanied the boat on trips of over twenty miles from its base, flying to the banks of the river from time to time to forage for food but always rejoining the boat before it got out of range. This was in December when presumably the birds were not breeding so that the attachment was to the nest and not to young. The presence of a nest is of prime importance as far as pair formation is concerned; I have already indicated that this can occur in two ways: either by mate replacement, when one member of an established pair with a nest dies, or by a young male taking up an unoccupied site and calling at it to attract an unmated female. Let us now examine these in more detail.

After the breeding season and the break-up of the grain-field flocks, the adult pairs return to their nests. If one member of a pair dies during this post-breeding period, the other still retains possession of the nest and in a very short time usually obtains a new mate. Although I have seen this happening many times, in only one case was the new mate a ringed bird. This involved a male who had been unsuccessful in obtaining a mate during the previous breeding season; when a hen returned to her nest in September without her mate, this cock at once left the nest he had been holding and joined up with her. It is difficult to believe, however, that all of the pair formations that occur in the autumn only concern adult birds; some of the new mates are probably young birds from the earlier broods of that year.

Replacements of lost mates occur in this way in September and

October, but sexual activity dies down after this and if one partner dies the remaining bird usually stays unmated until late January or February when pair formation begins again. From this time right through the breeding season until July much pair formation takes place by mate replacement in this way. As it is rather unlikely that both members of the pair will die in the period August–September or November–January, when little pair formation takes place, the majority of pairs are formed by mate replacement.

Pair formation between two first-year birds nevertheless does occur. To some extent it must be influenced by the availability of nest sites; where there is a surplus, young cocks can readily find a vacant site in the spring and by calling at this may be able to attract a mate. In other areas where nest sites are scarce it is only when one becomes vacant, by both members of a pair dying about the same time, that a young cock can obtain a site and call at it. However, in areas where sites are plentiful there is a tendency for pairs to hold more than one and hence it may be difficult even here for a first-year cock to find a vacant hole.

An unmated male with a nest spends much time at it, conspicuously in view and uttering the familiar chirrup call. The longer the bird is unsuccessful in obtaining a mate, the more persistent the calling becomes and if a hen comes near he will call ecstatically and shiver his wings in the solicitation behaviour described in the previous chapter and even follow her some distance away from the nest, continuing his posturing and calling. If the hen remains near the nest, the cock flies in and out of the hole; at first she is unwilling to approach too closely and shows her nervousness by flicking her tail. The cock's behaviour is clearly innate. The purpose is obviously to show the nest hole to the hen; on the other hand, his instinct is to defend it against intruders and, if the hen approaches too closely or attempts to follow him in, his attitude at once changes to threat. However, if the hen is persistent, ambivalence soon disappears and the cock freely accepts her. Once he has obtained a mate the cock still uses the chirrup call to proclaim ownership of the site, but the ecstatic calling is given up. A hen left in possession of a nest when her mate dies will also call at it, but this is a soft and subdued version of the cock's strident chirrup and is not as conspicuous; moreover a hen with a nest is seldom left for long without acquiring a new mate. According to T. H. Nelson in the days when bounties were offered for sparrows (see Chapter 18) the gunners used to shoot only the male of a pair; the hen then got another mate and it was possible in this way to kill no less than seven males at one nest—this illustrates how rapidly pair formation can take place.

It may be of interest to compare pair formation in the two areas where intensive studies were made. In the rural area there was clearly a shortage of holes and I have no records of a pair being able to hold more than one site. Here, when nesting boxes were put up, they were readily used. In the suburban area, on the other hand, where houses were much more numerous, although the sparrow population was also higher, there was clearly a surplus of suitable holes and a number were left vacant every year. These vacant sites attracted young cocks in the spring and it is possible that in the suburban area there was a greater proportion of cocks unable to obtain mates, preferring to retain their own nest hole to leaving this to look for an unmated hen with a nest; certainly out of eleven pair formations in the rural area only one did not take place by replacement, whereas in the suburban area the proportion was nine out of fifty-two. From the speed at which bereaved birds obtain new mates it appears that there is a considerable reservoir of unmated birds of both sexes available to fill any gap that occurs. I have known two cases of cocks obtaining new mates in July when their existing mates had lost interest in further breeding. In one case after the new mate had reared a successful brood both hens returned to the nest in the autumn on the break-up of the grain-field flock and a dispute developed over the nest; the younger wife eventually won and she remained to breed with the cock the following year.

Fig. 7, p. 46, shows the seasonal distribution of the formation of pairs for the sixty-three cases observed in both study areas. It will be seen that pair formation by mate replacement occurred in all months except December. It starts in a small way in January, quickly rises to a peak in February and March as the birds come into breeding condition, and takes place right through the breeding season as losses occur. Immediately after the moult in autumn there is a recrudescence of sexual behaviour and mates that have disappeared since the end of the breeding season are quickly replaced; only in December, when all sexual activities are at a low ebb, is there no replacement. The formation of pairs by young birds begins in February and continues well into the breeding season; on the average the first-year birds probably reach breeding condition rather later in the season than the adults, consequently some pairs are not formed until May. A few new pairs are formed in October.

The following table gives an illustration of the way that mates changed at one nest over a period of five years.

Date	♂*	♀*	Remarks
1.4.54	202	165	Observations began
Summer 54	202	165	1 brood reared
13.2.55	202	165	♀ 165 last seen
27.2.55	202	320	New ♀ appeared, probably first year bird
Summer 55	202	320	1 brood reared
8.12.55	202	320	♂ 202 last seen
11.2.56	n.r.	320	New ♂ appeared (not ringed)
Summer 56	n.r.	320	2 broods reared
22.7.56	n.r.	320	♂ last seen
16.9.56	370	320	New ♂ appeared; this bird was born in 1955 and held a nest from the late autumn of 1955 but failed to breed
9.2.57	370	320	♀ 320 last seen
17.2.57	370	520	New ♀ appeared (first-year bird)
Summer 57	370	520	2 broods reared
22.6.57	370	520	♂ 370 last seen
30.6.57	n.r.	520	New ♂ appeared, ♀ still feeding young of 2nd brood in nest
Summer 58	n.r.	520	2 broods reared

* a numbered bird indicates a colour-ringed individual; n.r. indicates not ringed.

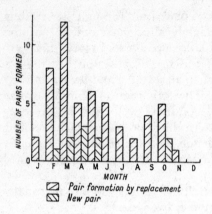

Pair formation by replacement
New pair

FIG. 7. Seasonal distribution of pair formation.

It will be seen that in this period five replacements of mates took place: new cocks appeared in February, June and September; new hens appeared in two different Februarys. It is interesting to notice that although a pair was formed by a new cock appearing in the breeding season (June 1957) no further breeding occurred; the pair held together until the following year when they reared two broods.

Observations at another nest give a rather different picture, the same pair breeding together for four years.

Date	♂	♀	Remarks
1.4.54	163	174	Observations began
Summer 54	163	174	1 brood reared
Summer 55	163	174	2 broods reared
Summer 56	163	174	2 broods reared
Summer 57	163	174	2 broods reared
2.2.58	163	174	♂ 163 last seen
15.2.58	698	174	New ♂ appeared
26.4.58	698	174	♀ 174 last seen at nest
17.5.58	698	n.r.	New ♀ appeared
Summer 58	698	n.r.	2 broods reared

♀ 174 lived for another month after she had deserted the nest but was probably too old by now to breed any more. The original pair were faithful to each other and to the nest site for at least four years. Usually one and sometimes both of the pair roosted in the nest at night over this period.

Although the generalisation that pairs are faithful to each other and to their nest sites for life is a reasonably accurate one, exceptions do occur. As already mentioned some pairs may hold more than one site and use both for breeding. Bigamy and desertions also occur but neither of these are common. The latter usually involves hens that lose their mates in the immediate post-breeding period; the attachment to nest site is less strong in the female than in the male and his absence after the return from autumn flocking, when attachment is in any case at its lowest ebb, may cause her to desert and take up with an unmated cock in possession of a nest.

One pair that bred together for four years used two nests about five feet apart. This pair was probably formed from two first-year birds in 1954; only one brood was reared that year though the birds paid some attention to the other site. The nests were used in the following way over the period of four years:

	Brood No.		
	1	2	3
1954	A	—	—
1955	B	A	B
1956	A	A	—
1957	B	A	B

Only in 1955 did a young cock attempt to take over one of the sites; this bird was seen at Nest A on several occasions in January but he made no real effort to displace the owner and eventually settled down at another site where he obtained a mate and bred successfully. I have other records of pairs using two sites in this way, and Prof. J. D. Craggs observed similar behaviour among the colour-ringed Hilbre breeding population, but in none of these did the partnership last as long as in the above case, nor was the transference from one nest to the other quite so clear cut. For instance, a pair which bred together for the years 1956–8 laid two clutches in one nest in 1956; two clutches in 1957, the first in the same nest, the second in a new one and in 1958 two clutches in the second nest. This involved only a change of nest site in the middle of the 1957 breeding season to a new hole about three yards away, though the birds continued to visit the original site.

Desertion of a mate once the pair bond has been sealed by rearing a brood must be rare, if it occurs at all (I have no records of this happening), though occasionally when one bird of a pair dies the remaining bird may move to another site. Bigamy is, I consider, rather exceptional in the house sparrow. For several breeding seasons I have had each year on average over twenty nests under close observation. In six of these years there was no evidence of bigamy; in the seventh (1957), on the other hand, no less than five cases occurred in the twenty-nine nests that were used for breeding. There is considerable evidence to show that the sexes are about equal in numbers with, if anything, a slight pre-ponderance of males (see Appendix v). The cock shares very fully in breeding duties, incubating the eggs and feeding the young almost as much as the hen; thus it is unlikely that he would be able to retain another nest site and mate without neglecting his family duties in the face of competition from other males. It can only be concluded that in 1957 there was a shortage of males in my study area, so that as mated cocks died other cocks already with mates and sites were able to take over. In most cases the bigamous cocks held two nests quite close to each other. In general, the bigamous pairs were very unsuccessful. Although I have seen hens rearing a family by themselves after their mate had died, the efforts of both birds are usually required to feed the young. In the case of the bigamous pairs the cocks tended to concentrate on one of the mates with the consequence that the young in the other nests were neglected and died. No doubt bigamous pairs could both produce young but it would require a very favourable combination of plentiful food and careful timing of the broods in the two nests. It is important that the cock co-operates in feeding the young for the first few days otherwise the hen is liable to desert. Mrs. D. Champkin informed me of several cases of bigamy that she observed; in most cases it appeared, that when both nests had young at the same time at least one of the broods failed, though if the timing was just right, one brood following the other by about seven to ten days, young fledged from both nests.

There is a case in America in which two females mated to the same male together laid eight eggs in the one nest-box; these eggs hatched successfully, the incubating and feeding duties being shared by the three parents. T. Pearse reports another instance of two hens laying in the same nest-box on Vancouver Island; the

PLATE 3. House sparrows in flight: *above*, male; *below*, female. The reduction in the extent of the black bib after the moult can be seen by comparing the male in this plate with that in Plate 1. (*E. Hosking*)

PLATE 4. Males can be seen at all times of the year at the entrances to their nests. (*J. Markham*)

clutches were separated by about five days but as the hens were shot no egg reached the stage of hatching.

There is a widely held view that the sparrow is immoral—Angelo in *Measure for Measure* says: "Sparrows must not build in his house-eaves because they are lecherous" or Chaucer's Summoner who was "as lecherous as a sparwe". My experience does not support this; out of hundreds of observations of faithfulness of pairs I have only once seen a hen allowing more than one cock to mate with her. I cannot, however, resist the temptation to carry this piece of anthropomorphism further and describe an instance of flirtation I saw in October 1952: a cock, who had bred earlier that year, was seen displaying to a first-year hen in an apple tree; suddenly he stopped and began self-consciously to preen—his mate had arrived in the tree!

Although the nest is probably the main factor in maintaining the pair, it is clear from many observations that the birds recognise each other when away from the nest and behave differently to their mates than towards other birds. For example, I have watched a cock feeding on a bone and keeping other sparrows of both sexes from joining him in the repast; yet when his mate arrived he made no demonstration towards her and allowed her to feed peacefully beside him. It is difficult to know just how far this individual recognition extends; in a colonial nester like the house sparrow it probably includes the near nesting neighbours. One observation shows that recognition is not merely confined to mated pairs: I had two males, which had been hand-reared from a few days old, together in my aviary; one of these escaped and was at liberty for two days before being recaptured. During this period the cock in the aviary became very excited and shivered his wings as soon as the other bird appeared in the garden or even flew over. This behaviour was confined to the appearance of the escaped bird, other sparrows being ignored, and it is clear that the bird in the aviary recognised his erstwhile companion even at a distance of some yards. A. Daanje also records how two rival cocks recognised each other when away from the nest and started to fight when they met.

Observation shows that the adults certainly recognise their

young when they are out of the nest; young birds, if hungry, will solicit food from any adult bird; while these may show some interest, they will not, in normal circumstances, feed any but their own young. I do not know whether this recognition is by sight or sound. In an enclosed nest the adults have little opportunity of seeing their young until they are old enough to come to the nest entrance to be fed and up to this stage strange young of the right age introduced to the nest appear to be accepted freely; this suggests that the strangers are not distinguished from the offspring by the sound of their voices. However, there is no need for recognition in natural circumstances at this stage and the way in which it is accomplished may not develop until the young are almost ready to fledge. The qualification "in normal circumstances" must, however, be inserted into the statement that adult sparrows do not feed any but their own young, because I have seen adult sparrows feeding young house martins in a nest and cases have been reported of sparrows feeding nestling blue tits, spotted flycatchers and fledgling dunnocks; so that it is not improbable that at times they will feed other young sparrows than their own.

In a discussion on pair formation, mention must be made of nest-site selection since on occasions there may be an association between the two. Clearly in the majority of cases of pairing, which take place by the replacement of a lost mate, no selection of a nest site is involved—on the other hand the young cock that adopts a hole and calls at it to attract a mate can be said to select the site. The hen also plays some part in this as the cock that adopts an unsuitable type of site has difficulty in attracting a mate. The thing that attracts the hen sparrow appears to be not merely "a calling and displaying cock" but "a calling and displaying cock with a suitable nest site"; thus the hen has the final say in selection—after all it is she who lays the eggs. I have known a number of holes in breeding areas that have been regularly adopted by cocks in the spring but though these cocks have called strongly at their hole and although they have been able to attract a hen they have never succeeded in keeping one, with the result that these holes have never been used for breeding. Presumably they have been unsuitable—perhaps because they were too small or were at the edge of or outside a breeding colony—and for that reason have been rejected by the hens. Occasionally early in the year a pair may be formed at one of these unsuitable sites but as the breeding season approaches the hen deserts or the pair moves off to find a better hole; for example, L. R. Lewis tells me of a pair that adopted the open end of a piece of tubular scaffolding early in the breeding season and were there regularly for about a week, the cock calling and both birds carrying grass to the hole, before giving up the site. In a case like this, when a pair that has already formed goes off together to find a new site, it is difficult to suggest which member of the pair selects the new nest.

CHAPTER 6

NESTS AND NEST BUILDING

ALL OF the true sparrows (genus *Passer*) build domed nests. The house sparrow prefers the protection of a hole and nests are most frequently to be found under the eaves of houses (Plate 7a, p. 80) and in other suitable holes and crevices in buildings, including the nests of house martins and those of other species with similar nesting habits, namely the cliff swallow in America and the fairy martin in Australia. The next most favoured site is in creepers on the walls of buildings (Plate 8b, p. 81). Nests are also built in the branches of trees, particularly thick hawthorns and evergreens, and in the walls of the nests of large birds, for example rooks and magpies in Britain, storks and birds of prey abroad, though this habit is less frequent than in the related Spanish and tree sparrows. Natural tree holes are not commonly used in Britain (Plate 9, p. 96), probably merely because the house sparrow prefers to nest on or close to man's buildings and presumably suitably placed tree holes are not common, though the bird has been seen apparently attempting to make good this deficiency by excavating a hole in the end of a rotten branch. I have known house sparrows come into competition with tree sparrows over holes in trees near buildings (tree holes are the most common sites used by tree sparrows in Britain); in this case the house sparrow is usually successful over its slightly smaller and, in this country at least, rather shyer relative. Unusual sites that have been reported are lamp-posts and open-topped nests in hedgerows, such as those of song thrushes and greenfinches, which are domed over by the sparrows.

In wilder country, as on the islands round the coast of Britain, sites in caves and cliffs are also used; holes in stone walls have been reported, though in practically all cases the nests have been within a few hundred yards of an occupied house. R. Gray described an enormous concentration nesting in holes in a sandstone quarry near Glasgow in the last century. In other parts of its range, particularly in Asia, cliffs and even earth banks appear to be commonly used: house sparrows have not infrequently been found nesting in sand martins' holes in Europe and America; in Egypt, kingfishers' holes have been reported. The members of the genus *Passer* are generally tree nesters but with a strong tendency to use securer sites and many of the species nest in holes in the walls and roofs of buildings; the house sparrow, though still, and probably originally, a tree nester, is pre-eminently the occupier of holes in buildings and thus it is likely that the adoption of cliff sites has developed from this habit.

Open tree sites seem to be used when other sites are not available and also appear to be commoner in the warmer parts of the bird's range. We have seen how the nest plays a very big part in the bird's life and is used year after year. Nests in trees are liable to be dislodged by storms in the winter (Plate 11a, p. 112) and later, in the spring, material is stolen from them by other birds when the owners are absent, hence a securer site is obviously to be preferred. This is confirmed by observations made in my rural study area. When I began to watch there, several tree nests were in use in a deodar close to my house. A number of nest-boxes were put up one autumn on the tree and on the walls of the house nearby. The birds kept their tree nests and maintained them throughout the winter but as the breeding season approached they moved to the nest-boxes and built in them; the tree nests were abandoned and no further breeding took place in tree nests during my observations in this area—one spring a cock did build a nest in a tree; he did not, however, obtain a mate after calling at the nest for some time and gave up the site. It would appear that tree sites had been used because of a shortage of suitable holes; the provision of nest-boxes made no significant difference in the breeding population and thus it would appear that this was not dependent on the availability of holes for use as nest sites. It is interesting that, for the first twenty years after the bird was introduced to the United States, tree nests were very uncommon; by 1870 when the numbers of sparrows started to build up, and presumably suitable sites in holes in some areas had become scarce, tree nests began to be more and more commonly reported. Scarcity of holes is not, however, the full story. K. Greve found on Heligoland that in 1958 out of a total population of 180 pairs, twenty-one were nesting in trees, although there appeared to be no shortage of holes in buildings; a further four pairs bred in the walls of magpies' nests.

In the Far East, where the house sparrow is absent, the tree sparrow has filled the role of a "house sparrow", breeding in what to us are typical house sparrow sites. In parts of its range in the east, e.g. North Pakistan, Afghanistan and Russian Turkestan, the house sparrow is a summer visitor, while the tree sparrow is a resident. Here the normal roles are reversed, the tree sparrow breeding in the houses, the house sparrow in holes in banks and in cliffs. Tree sites also appear to be commoner in the eastern part of the bird's range.

In all situations the nest is basically the same, consisting of an outer layer of dead grass or straw with a lining of softer materials. The nest is domed* and in an unrestricted site it is approximately the size of a football with the entrance hole in the side (Plate 7b, p. 80). In restricted sites, where the size is limited, a domed nest is still built and grass is added until the cavity is completely filled (Plate 8a, p. 81), though if the hole used is very small the nest may be reduced to a mere lining. The grass ball is lined with feathers and to a lesser extent with other materials, such as hair, string, fine grasses (including lawn mowings), paper and especially bast, which is torn off twigs and small branches. The birds will expend a lot of energy doing this, tugging and jerking at the loose ends until a strip is torn free; at times bushes and trees can be quite disfigured in this way. If in urban areas, chicken feathers are put out at the beginning of the breeding season, they are quickly taken by the birds and incorporated into their nests; traps can be successfully baited with feathers when nest building is taking place. Sparrows have even been recorded plucking feathers for their nests from the flanks of wood and feral pigeons. One industrious observer counted almost one thousand two hundred feathers in the lining of a single nest, though two hundred or three hundred are more common. When a house martin's nest is taken over both grass and feathers are added by the sparrows and the usurped nests can

---

* Occasionally the nest is not roofed over (Plates 8b, p. 81 and 10, p. 97); possibly this is an evolutionary trend in a bird that now most regularly builds in enclosed sites.

readily be distinguished by the grasses hanging down from the entrance.

Nests are usually at least ten feet from the ground, though there are records of a nest in a hawthorn hedge only three feet above ground level and another only a few inches from the ground in a gorse bush. Where tree nests are built, quite large colonies may be formed (Plate 12, p. 113); for example, G. I. Westcott gives an instance of seventeen nests in a moderately sized pear tree. When crowded together in this way the entrances may be only a few inches apart. From the exterior, the nest appears very untidy, but it is reasonably well woven together and secure against the weather.

Nest building can be seen at almost any time of the year, though it is naturally most common at the beginning of the breeding season. Young cocks that have taken up new holes in the spring frequently start building before they have got mates—the presence of a nest as well as a nest site appears to be of importance in attracting and retaining a mate. At first, as is common with the development of a new pattern of behaviour, the movements are incomplete, the nesting material is picked up in the bill, but the bird apparently does not quite know what to do with it and it is dropped again. Next the material is carried to the nest, but dropped there rather aimlessly; soon however, it is taken into the nest hole or placed in the chosen spot if the nest is being built in the branches of a tree. Once the pair has been formed both birds take part in building, though the cock still does most of the work—when A. J. Berger removed a nest from a nest-box after the first brood had flown, the cock alone built the complete nest for the second brood, the first egg of which was laid nine days after the previous brood had fledged—and the nest may be virtually complete some time before eggs are laid. When necessary a pair with a site can build a complete nest in a sudden burst of activity lasting only two or three days—A. W. Boyd records how, after a gutter was cleared on 11th July, two fresh nests were started and contained one and three eggs respectively two days later. After the outer structure has been finished the birds continue to bring lining material until eggs are laid and regularly when the eggs are being incubated; I have, however, known one or two cases in which eggs have been laid on the bare floor of a nest-box with only the suggestions of a cup of grass, yet by the time the young had hatched the nest-box had been filled with a complete domed nest with its lining of feathers.

With the return to the nests in autumn after the moult, nest building is again quite common. Here the sexes frequently have completely different views; the cock is anxious to add something to the nest while at this time of year the hen likes removing any excess rubbish that has accumulated in the hole. Several times I have watched a pair at odds in this way, the cock collecting the rubbish the hen is chucking out and taking it back in again. Nests that have already been used require little attention beyond the addition of a few feathers in the spring if they are in secure sites; nests in open sites in trees require regular maintenance throughout the winter months if they are not to disappear.

The carrying of nesting material has frequently led to reports of breeding at all seasons of the year. Breeding certainly does occur outside the normal breeding season but not as often as might be inferred from building activities; much of this is merely titivation of the nest, though it should be mentioned that in parts of its range where winter conditions are severe the birds build roost nests. These are nests that are built in autumn and early winter in holes that are too small for breeding; like normal nests they are warmly lined with feathers. While they have not been commonly reported in Britain, where the winters are generally not severe, the building of roost nests seems to be more common in Germany and further north. This is a most interesting adaptation, allowing the bird to retain its sedentary habits and survive the long, cold winter nights in high latitudes in places where there is sufficient food in the immediate neighbourhood of man's houses to enable it to pick up a living during the daylight hours. S. C. Kendeigh's observation that house sparrows are only able to live for about fifteen hours at freezing point shows how essential this behaviour is at latitudes where winter temperatures are low and the nights in that season exceed fifteen hours. The building of roost nests at high altitudes with cold winters, for example at Leadville, Colorado, U.S.A. (10,200 ft.), has also been reported. It is of interest to note, however, that the cape sparrow also builds roost nests, though its range is restricted to a region lying between 18° and 35° south of the equator, where the climate is sub-tropical.

House sparrows do not hold large territories, but the nest and the immediately surrounding area are strongly defended against other sparrows; defence at all times is intra-sexual, the males only attack males and the females only females. The owners threaten rivals that approach within a few inches of the nest entrance or attempt to enter; this is usually enough to deter the stranger but very occasionally severe and prolonged fighting may take place. For example, on 30th April, 1952, two males were watched fighting over a nest for nearly an hour; one of these birds had been displaced by another male from his nest and he in turn was attempting to oust the other bird. In this, however, he was quite unsuccessful and, I think, would have been killed if I had not interfered on one occasion when the new owner was holding him down on the ground with his feet and was attempting to peck at his eyes. This was a first-year bird and a few days later he managed to re-establish himself at the nest from which he had been displaced and subsequently bred there. A severe battle over a nest was seen between two females on 19th April, 1953. This lasted for about an hour and took place mostly in the gutter above the nest; both birds lost feathers in the encounter and once they fell from the gutter locked together, bounced off the garage roof below and did not separate until they reached the ground. Immediately they both flew back to the nest and the fight continued. Fights of this severity are, however, rare (though a case of one cock killing another and eating its brains has been reported) and usually a threat posture is enough to deter the other bird; if the bird so threatened flies off he is usually pursued by the owner and a long aerial chase may result, though when the birds finally land they ignore each other and an attack is not pressed home, no doubt because the stimulus provided by the territory is now lacking.

CHAPTER 7

SEXUAL DISPLAY

THE FORMATION of pairs, the acquiring of nest sites and the building of nests are a necessary prelude to breeding; with the house sparrow these may precede breeding by many months, though all are intensified as the breeding season approaches. Another activity, which, as I shall show, is an integral part of the breeding cycle, is the boisterous behaviour variously known as "Sparrow Weddings", "Sparrow Parties" and more soberly as communal or group display. A good impression of it is given by Peter Quennell in "Small Birds":

> Small birds who sweep into a tree
> —A storm of fluttering, stilled as suddenly,
> Making the light slip round a shaken berry,
> Swinging slim sunlight twigs uncertainly,
> Are moved by rippling of light discontent
> —Quick waves of anger, breaking through the tree
> Into a foam of riot—voices high
> And tart as a sloe-berry.

Although the display has been many times described accurately by scientific naturalists its significance is to some extent still in doubt. I shall discuss it in some detail and show how it fits into the life of the sparrow before attempting to suggest what purpose it fulfils.

Attention is usually attracted to the display by the noisy chirruping of a group of sparrows or the sight of a small party in rapid, close, chasing flight disappearing into a hedge bottom or other cover. Closer inspection reveals that whereas up to a dozen or even more cocks may be involved only one hen is present. Clearly if we are to understand the reasons for the display it is important to see how the familiar, noisy, scrapping party arises.

Although I have watched and made notes on literally thousands of displays, I have seen the beginnings of only comparatively few. The start usually involves a bird of each sex with the cock displaying to the hen by hopping near her in the "standing to attention" posture described in Chapter 4 and bowing before her in rather a stately fashion. In this posture he hops towards the hen and then turns and faces away; if he approaches too closely she threatens him by elongating her body and pressing it downwards with the head stretched forward. If the cock comes within range the hen gapes at him and may lunge forward pecking at his nape and wings. This behaviour may attract the attention of nearby males, particularly if the cock is uttering the strident chirrup call, which then fly down and join in. Usually there comes a stage when the hen attempts to escape by flight and a noisy chase is initiated with the excitedly calling cocks in close pursuit; this rapid chase attracts further cocks and so the displaying party grows. Once the hen lands the cocks immediately begin to call and posture in front of her in the way already described. The hen now defends herself vigorously and may attack the males quite violently; according to A. Daanje, the more aggressively the hen behaves the more intense is the display of the cocks. In a protracted display the hen may make several attempts to escape with the cocks following like a pack of hounds; each time she lands the others land close to her posturing excitedly. The hen appears to be quite frightened and tries to find a secure place from which she can defend herself—I have seen one retreat under a stone in a rockery and another flee into a nest-box. This has taken some time to describe but in fact the whole performance may only take half a minute and rarely lasts more than twice this before the cocks begin to lose interest and move away.

This is the general pattern though it may vary in details. A feature that has been frequently noticed is that the cocks attempt to peck at the cloaca of the hen—this suggests a sexual significance in the display. When there are a large number of cocks only a small proportion may take an "active" part, the remainder merely occupying the role of spectators. The sexual significance of the display is also borne out by its seasonal frequency and by the variation in the average number of birds taking part. The seasonal frequencies for 1955 and 1957 for the suburban study area are given in Figure 8, which shows the number of displays recorded in each half month period. I have kept records of displays for seven years and in each year the seasonal variation in the number was very similar. From the beginning of January there is a rapid build-up in the number of displays, reaching a sharp peak in March (second half) or April, followed by an equally sharp decline; in some years there is a distinct second peak later in the breeding season. In all years there is an almost complete cessation of displays in August and the beginning of September; this is followed by a minor recrudescence in the autumn, reaching a peak at the end of October. A. Daanje gives a very similar seasonal pattern, though as his results are given only on a monthly basis the separate peaks during the breeding season are not shown.

The pattern is closely related to the annual sexual cycle. In Britain the start of the breeding season does not vary much from year to year: in six out of the seven years, in which I kept detailed records on the two breeding colonies, twenty-five per cent of the first clutches were laid in the period 25th to 30th April; in each of these years the first peak in the frequency of displays fell in the first half of April. In the other year, 1957, after a mild open winter, a quarter of the first clutches were laid by 20th April and the display peak came at the end of March. The main influence of bad weather seems to be to prolong the period in which first clutches are laid (probably by delaying the breeding of first-year birds); in these years the second peak in the display is merged out. The autumn peak matches the recrudescence of sexual behaviour that occurs particularly in sedentary species at this time and is shown in the house sparrow internally by a minor growth in testicular activity (curves of testis volume and interstitial cell cycles for house sparrows in Belfast, Northern Ireland, obtained by L. T. Threadgold correspond closely with those of Fig. 8) and externally by nest-site prospecting and nest building.

The average number of birds taking part follows a somewhat similar pattern to that of the frequency, Fig. 9, p. 62. Displays on the average are larger in the months just preceeding the breeding season and it is only in March and the beginning of April that ones involving ten or more birds have been seen. A minimum in the

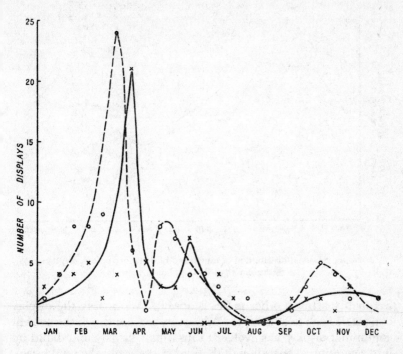

FIG. 8. Seasonal distribution of displays.
x 1955   o 1957

average number of birds taking part occurs at the end of the
breeding season; this is followed by an increase during the period
of autumn recrudescence.

In two papers published on the displays of the house sparrow
I put forward the view that those involving only one male were
quite distinct from the so-called communal displays involving two
or more males. I no longer believe this to be the case. Pair displays
occur most often when both the frequency of communal displays
and the number of birds taking part is low; again, in those displays
in which there are only two birds, it is usually found that the hen
has not tried to escape by flight, so that the sexual chase that

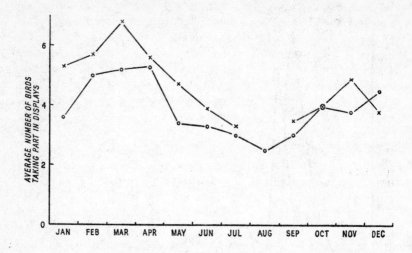

FIG. 9. Seasonal distribution of number of birds taking part in displays.
o Suburban 1954–8   x Rural 1949–53

frequently attracts other males is absent. Presumably the display of a single cock to a hen is the original type from which the present communal display has evolved; thus a pair display may build up into a communal one, though this is not necessarily always the case. Since it appears that the motivation and the function of both the displays involving one and those involving a number of males are the same, I have included the pair displays in the results shown graphically in Figs. 8 and 9.

Before we can attempt to interpret the significance of the display in the life of the house sparrow it is necessary to know something of the relationships of the individuals taking part. Even in a population in which the majority of the birds are colour-ringed this has been no easy matter: the display usually takes place in a bush or under cover where the birds are not easily seen; again it is only of comparatively short duration and frequently involves headlong chases from one piece of cover to another. However, I have identified sufficient individuals to be able to make the following generalisations. In most of the displays the mate of the hen is one of the main participants; this is not always the case, however, and a few involving a mated hen but not her mate have been recorded— on one occasion I saw a hen fly to her nest immediately after a display and be mounted there by her mate who had not taken part. Unmated adult hens may also be the centre of the display and the cocks taking part include both single and mated birds, the latter even when they have a nest with eggs or young.

I believe the display may arise in a number of ways. The first and most important is when a cock attempts to mount his mate when she is not willing to accept him—a number of workers in America have shown by histological examination of house sparrows that the males reach breeding condition on the average about three weeks in advance of the females. The hen repulses the cock's advances by adopting the threat display. The cock keeps his distance and postures in front of his mate in the sexual display attitude; if, however, the hen flies off she is at once pursued and this sexual chase attracts other sexually mature males in the vicinity to join in. An observation on 23rd April, 1953 illustrates this: an adult pair, which had bred together the previous year, were in a tree a few feet from their nest; the cock attempted to mount; the hen flew off followed by the cock and three other males joined in. This hen was also seen at the centre of a display on 17th April, though on this occasion none of the males taking part was identified. Successful coition with the hen was first seen on 26th April and was observed regularly from then until 8th May, when the first egg was laid. The next most common initiation results from an unpaired cock displaying at a hen that comes near his nest; this is presumably an attempt at pair formation by the cock. If the hen is unwilling (she may be an already mated bird) she attacks the cock and then, if she flies off, the cock gives chase and a communal display arises in the way already described. Another interesting case involves a mated cock and a strange hen. Both members of a pair feed their young in the nest but as fledging approaches the cock sometimes begins to lose interest and may display at his mate inviting coition; if she does not respond, a thing she rarely does when the young are still in the nest, the cock may then display to a strange hen with the result as before.

Additional cocks are attracted to take part in the display either by the initial chase or subsequent chases involving several birds, or by the sight and sound of a displaying group; if there is no sexual chase the pair display frequently does not build up. The final type of display I call "induced" displays as they do not appear to have the same sexual content but are induced by the rapid flight of a group of birds; this may occur when a feeding flock of birds is suddenly disturbed, the resulting flight leading to a display, particularly at the peak seasons when the males are most sexually active. In these induced displays the birds sort themselves out in flight so that the resulting display is directed at one hen or on occasions two displaying groups may form round separate hens. An incident reported by L. R. Lewis in which three male house sparrows were seen in a noisy chase with a blue tit probably arose in a similar way.

The function of the display is clearly that of sexual stimulation: this is shown by the way the periods of most frequent and intense displays immediately precede periods of egg laying in the colony; (this has already been indicated, but further details are given in Chapter 8 and Fig. 12, p. 71). Sexual development in the male, leading to spermatogenesis, occurs as a response to external stimuli, in particular in temperate climates to changing daylength; the sexual development of the female occurs later than in the male and does not advance to ovulation without such additional stimuli as the presence of a male with a suitable nest site, nesting material (E. Polikarpova has shown that for a female house sparrow to reach ovulation in an aviary it was necessary not only to provide a male but also a nest and nesting material) and courtship display— the communal display is in fact the house sparrow's courtship. In many passerines, pairs are not formed, or at least nest sites are not selected and nests built, until immediately before the start of breeding; these activities by themselves, or associated with some form of display, may act as courtship. As we have seen in the house sparrow, pair formation and nest building may precede breeding by many months so that some separate courtship behaviour is very important. The fact that this courtship is a communal one results from the social behaviour and colonial nesting of the bird so that a

PLATE 5. Young house sparrow begging food from female in the wing-shivering solicitation posture. (*C. W. Teager*)

PLATE 6. Communal activities: *above*, water bathing; *below*, dust bathing.
(*C. W. Teager*)

male inviting a female to coition must do this in the sight of other sexually mature males, which are stimulated to join in. In strongly territorial species courtship between a pair has a stimulating effect on the neighbouring pairs but no communal display results because of the inhibiting effect of territorial behaviour, though even in territorial species trespassing by males does occur when courtship displays are taking place.

During an intense display the participants may be so oblivious of their surroundings—I have even had members of a displaying party fly into me during one of their headlong chases—that they become a prey to cats and motor cars. Hence it would appear that the communal display must serve some useful function otherwise it would have been eliminated by natural selection and replaced by some other form of courtship less harmful to the species. I think the main benefit is synchronisation of breeding.* The sight of a pair copulating, which takes place at the nest in full view of other pairs, has a strong sexually stimulating effect on the other males; because of the communal display the females of these pairs have also reached full sexual development and are willing to accept their mates, who would otherwise interfere with the coition of the mating pair. Just before the beginning of breeding, it can frequently be seen how coition by one pair will initiate similar behaviour in other nearby pairs.

The house sparrow, as I shall show later, has a tropical origin and it is just possible that the communal display with its mutual stimulation leading to breeding synchronisation may have originated in the tropics where seasonal changes in daylength and other factors have not the same significance in determining the breeding season. If so, it has been retained in temperate regions because of the advantages discussed above.

In the autumn, after the refractory period of the gonads that follows breeding, there is, particularly in sedentary species that do not have to undergo the severe physical strain of migration, a recrudescence of the male gonads that may even lead to spermato-

---

* Social stimulation leading to synchronisation of breeding has been suggested by Fraser Darling for colonial nesting sea-birds, the advantage in this case being to shorten the period when vulnerable eggs and young are available to predators.

genesis. It is clear that this is responsible for the recrudescence of communal displays which occurs in October and November; only rarely do these stimulate the females to ovulation and with the regression of all sexual activities at the winter solstice displays become infrequent.

Once the period of courtship is over and the hen is ready for reproduction, coition becomes frequent. Display leading to successful coition is almost always initiated by the sexually mature hen; she prostrates herself in the invitation position with her head drawn in, wings slightly opened and shivered, and may utter a soft "tee-tee-tee" call. This is quite unlike the aggressive posture adopted in the communal display, when the bird holds herself erect and frequently lunges with opened bill at the posturing males. The cock seldom ignores his displaying mate and may be induced to mount as many as thirty or more times—as Laurence Sterne writes in his Sentimental Journey: "I remember the grave and learned Bevoriskius, in his Commentary upon the generations from Adam, very naturally breaks off in the middle of a note to give an account to the world of a couple of sparrows upon the out-edge of his window, which had incommoded him all the time he wrote, and at last had entirely taken him off from his genealogy. 'Tis strange!' writes Bevoriskius, 'but the facts are certain, for I have the curiosity to mark them down one by one with my pen—but the cock-sparrow, during the little time that I could have finished this note, has actually interrupted me with the reiteration of his caresses three-and-twenty times and a half. How merciful,' adds Bevoriskius, 'is Heaven to his creatures.'" The cock usually hops up towards the hen from about six to twelve inches away and then jumps on to her back; during coition he may peck at the hen's nape, sometimes so violently that feathers are removed and hens with bare napes can often be seen during the breeding season. On other occasions the cock may stretch over so that the pair touch bills. Between each mount the cock may preen, wipe his bill, peck at the roof or whatever he is standing on, or go through a variety of sinuous movements with his neck. As a result of the consummatory act sexual motivation, which has overcome fear or aggression towards the hen, is temporarily reduced and presumably these are displacement activities arising from ambivalence of the male's mood; such behaviour, originating in this way, could then have evolved with the function of stimulating the hen to further matings. Finally if the cock persists, the hen gives up her submissive posture and attacks her mate. During coition the "tee-tee-tee" call can usually be heard; this may be a solicitation call used by the hen, but it is also used by the cock as he runs up to mount.

Coition may occur between a mated pair up to three months before the first egg is laid. It becomes very frequent in the week before egg laying and may continue less regularly until the eggs hatch. It begins again once the brood has fledged, occasionally a day or so earlier, leading up to a subsequent clutch. Even if no further clutch is laid coition frequently occurs for a week or two after a brood has fledged. Coition usually takes place immediately beside the nest, though I have seen a pair mating as much as twenty-five yards away from it, and always above ground level.

Male house sparrows do not regularly feed their mates as a part of courtship, though food may occasionally be offered before the birds start breeding and sometimes, when they are feeding young, the male will pass food to the female. Again during nest building the male may occasionally pass building material to his mate. Courtship feeding, presentation of nesting material and displays of this sort are basically "appeasement" actions; they are probably less necessary in the house sparrow, in which pairs are formed for life, than in other species in which pairs are formed anew at the beginning of each breeding season.

CHAPTER 8

BREEDING

IN GREAT BRITAIN the breeding season extends from April to August, with early pairs starting in March and late ones extending into September. This is the general pattern in the northern hemisphere, the start of breeding getting later with increasing latitude as is shown in Fig. 10, which is based on rather broad statements culled from the literature of Europe and northern America. Information obtained in this way is by no means exact and no doubt factors other than latitude have an effect (e.g. hours of sunshine and temperature); nevertheless the over-riding effect of latitude is quite clear, breeding in the north of the bird's range starting about two months later than in the south. House sparrows introduced to the southern hemisphere have adapted themselves to local conditions: in temperate regions they breed from September to March, though nothing seems to have been recorded about the way in which this transition was achieved; in south-eastern Brazil, on the other hand, they breed in the dry season, which is from March to October, the same time of year as their European relatives. In Europe and America, in addition to the fairly well defined breeding season, cases of breeding have been recorded in all months of the year. Successful breeding has been recorded, for example, in Utah in January and March with the temperature below zero and heavy snow on the ground.

The seasonal distribution of the laying of clutches in Britain has been determined by S. Cramp from an analysis of nesting records collected by members of the British Trust for Ornithology; the results from 1,845 nests are summarised in Fig. 11 (p. 70). It will be seen that only a comparatively small proportion of clutches is started before the middle of April; breeding then proceeds rapidly, reaching a peak of intensity in the first half of May, and continues throughout the summer extending into August, though only a few clutches are laid in that month. The breeding season is

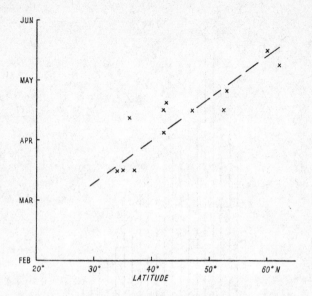

FIG. 10. Effect of latitude on the start of breeding season in Europe and N. America. The crosses are reported dates from both continents.

essentially the same throughout the British Isles, though the results indicate that it gets under way more rapidly in the south-west than in the south-east and that proportionately more clutches are laid in August in the north than in the south.

Fig. 12, p. 71, gives the number of clutches started each week in my rural study colony for 1953 and my suburban colony for 1957; first, second, third and fourth clutches are shown separately. The dates have in many cases been obtained from observations on the behaviour of the birds and not by examination of the nest, though checks at nest-boxes, where laying and hatching could be determined, have shown that it is possible to establish the date of laying and hatching in this way with negligible error. In six years that detailed observations were made the first peak came in the period 23rd April to 6th May, slightly earlier than Cramp's analysis suggests is typical for the British Isles. 1957 was somewhat

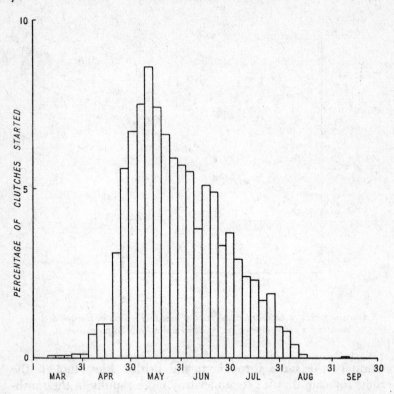

FIG. 11. Seasonal distribution of laying of clutches in Britain. (Based on analysis of British Trust for Ornithology Nest Record Cards by S. Cramp.)

unusual, however, in the early start to breeding even though the peak came at the normal time; this probably reflects the fact, already mentioned, that the 1957 breeding season followed an unusually mild and open winter. Cramp's results confirm that breeding started early in 1957 over the whole country.

An interesting feature from Fig. 12 is that there are three distinct cycles of breeding throughout the season. These, however, do not merely correspond to first, second and third clutches; the second peak, particularly in 1957 and also in other years not

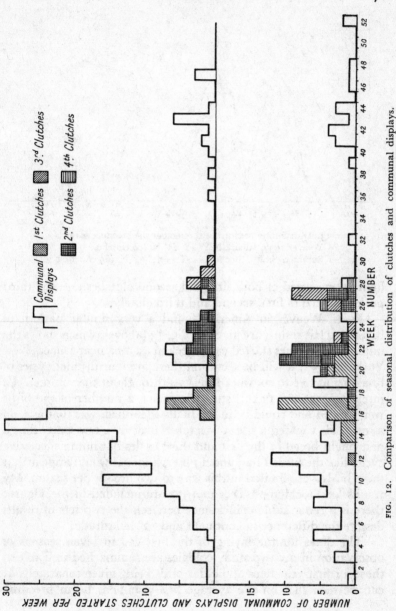

FIG. 12. Comparison of seasonal distribution of clutches and communal displays.

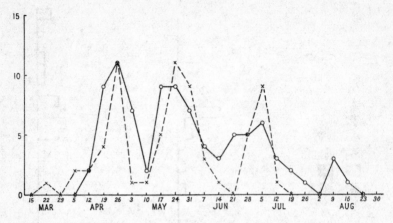

FIG. 13. Distribution of clutches throughout the breeding season.
o Weaver 1937, Ithaca, N.Y. 42° 25′ N. (89 clutches)
x Summers-Smith, Stockton-on-Tees 54° 34′ N. (65 clutches)

figured, consisted of both first and second clutches and the third
peak consisted of first, second and third clutches.

R. L. Weaver in America found a very similar pattern of
breeding. His results are given in Fig. 13 (above), which shows the
number of clutches started each week in an area near Ithaca, New
York, in 1937; it will be seen that there are four distinct cycles of
breeding at five to six week intervals throughout the summer. An
interesting feature of this study, in which a number of the birds
were ringed and could be individually identified, was that as soon
as one pair vacated a site it was taken over by a new pair; thus a
pair might breed in the first and third cycles but not in successive
cycles like the birds I had under observation. It would appear that
these birds were limited in this way to two broods per season. My
results for Stockton-on-Tees in 1957 are included in the Figure;
there is a remarkable coincidence between the two sets of results
despite the difference in continent and 12° in latitude.

The dates for the laying of the first egg in seven seasons of
observation in my two study colonies are summarised in Table 2,
those for first-year hens and older birds being given separately. It
can be seen that on the average first-year hens begin breeding

later than older birds. The majority of first-year hens do not lay until the second cycle of breeding. Those that lay in the first are usually, though not invariably, mated to cocks that have bred before. First-year cocks may not take up sites and mate till after the start of the breeding season; J. K. Stanford informs me that he regularly sees flocks of male house sparrows in Wiltshire up to the end of April, these presumably must be made up of first-year birds that have not yet paired.

TABLE 2

Differences in the Start of Breeding between
First-year and Older Females

| Study area | Number of birds | Start of first clutch | |
		Range	Mean date
Highclere 1952–3:			
1st year hens	16	20/4–27/7	20/5
2nd–5th year hens	9	18/4–12/5	27/4
Stockton 1954–8:			
1st year hens	31	9/4–24/6	12/5
2nd–5th year hens	34	25/3–20/5	28/4

The distribution of communal displays in 1953 and 1957 is included in Fig. 12 (p. 71), it can be seen that as soon as the first cycle of breeding begins there is a striking falling off in the number of displays. It appears that if the first-year pairs miss the first cycle of breeding then they have to await the stimulus of the second peak of displays, that comes once the first lot of broods has fledged, before they can begin breeding. In several years a number of first clutches have even been laid in the third cycle of breeding.

There is no clear suggestion in Cramp's analysis (Fig. 11) of the polymodal distribution of breeding found in my results and those of Weaver given in Fig. 13. As I shall show later, when discussing social behaviour (Chapter 10), breeding within colonies tends to be closely synchronised, though different colonies in the same area may vary by as much as two weeks or more, further, as

I have already indicated, the start of breeding may vary considerably from year to year; the effect of this would be to merge out the cycles of breeding in a large sample taken from all parts of the country over a period of years. If the pattern of breeding found in my colonies—namely, definite cycles of breeding, with most old birds laying at least two clutches and the majority of first-year birds not starting to breed until the second cycle—then the second cycle would be expected to have the maximum number of pairs laying. A closer examination of Cramp's results shows that this is in fact the case. If the period between broods is taken as forty days, which, as I shall show later is fairly typical, and the three cycles are assumed to fall in the periods 4th April to 13th May, 14th May to 22nd June and 23rd June to 1st August, as appears reasonable from Fig. 12, then the distribution of the start of clutches for the years 1954–8 in my Stockton colony agrees closely with Cramp's results:

	4th April–13th May	14th May–22nd June	23rd June–1st August
B.T.O. Nest Record Cards	34%	45%	19%
Summers-Smith 1954–8	31%	43%	25%

—the small difference could easily be explained by a slight waning in the enthusiasm of observers taking part in the British Trust for Ornithology survey towards the end of the summer, though it appears that this is hardly significant.

The number of clutches laid per pair per season is given for my two study colonies in Table 3; results for first year and older hens are given separately. It can be seen that birds lay fewer clutches in their first breeding season than in subsequent ones; this may well be a consequence of the later start of breeding of these birds. On Hilbre Island over a period of four breeding seasons J. D. Craggs found an average, from twenty pairs, of 2·1 clutches per year, a very similar result to those obtained in my colonies when all age groups are lumped together. The majority of birds lay two or three clutches, but I have three records of four clutches being laid by individual hens: in two cases these were second-year birds, in the third the hen was in her fourth year. I have four instances of hens surviving to their fifth breeding season: one of these successfully

raised two broods; one raised one brood before dying; the third
lost her mate, with whom she had bred in the four previous
seasons, just before the start of the fifth season, and, though she
mated again, no further brood was raised. It seems that hen house
sparrows are reaching the end of their procreative life after five
years. We might ask what it is that controls the number of broods.
Can it be that the birds having more broods have less chance of
survival by exposing themselves to the dangers associated with
feeding young for a longer period or do they merely as a result of
exhaustion have less chance of survival and hence in the long run
raise only the same number of young as birds with a fewer number
of broods per year, natural selection having evolved a balance,
which for the house sparrow in Britain works out between two and
three broods per year? It would be interesting to know whether the
number of broods reared per pair is density dependent, but
sufficient information is not available to test this.

TABLE 3

Number of Clutches per Season

| Study area | Number of birds laying | | | | Average |
	1 Clutch	2 Clutches	3 Clutches	4 Clutches	
Highclere					
1st yr. ♀♀	4	8	4	0	2·0
2nd–5th yr.	1	3	5	0	2·3
Stockton					
1st yr. ♀♀	11	16	4	0	1·8
2nd–5th yr.	3	18	10	3	2·3

For the most complete information on clutch size we must
again turn to Cramp's analysis of the British Trust for Ornithology
records. In Great Britain clutches of four are commonest, accounting for almost half of the ones reported, five is next with slightly
over a quarter and three making up approximately a sixth;
clutches of six and seven were recorded—only three cases of the

latter out of 702 nests—but like those smaller than three accounted for only an insignificant proportion of the total. The average clutch size in Britain is 4·1 and remains very nearly constant throughout the breeding season, rising from 4·0 in April to a maximum of 4·3 in the second half of June and then decreasing to slightly less than four towards the end of the summer. This variation is typical of many temperate region nesting birds with a prolonged breeding season and it has been suggested that it is an adaptation to a seasonal variation in the amount of food available for feeding the young or to changing daylength, which varies the time each day available for collecting food for the nestlings, though in the majority of species that have been investigated the change is much greater than that given above for the sparrow. No similar systematic study exists for other parts of the bird's range, though the evidence that is available from the United States suggests that the most frequent clutch size for the introduced house sparrow is five with six not uncommonly recorded; the average clutch size lies in the range 4·5 to 5, significantly larger than that in Britain. In Turkestan, where the house sparrow is a summer visitor laying only one clutch per year, clutches of seven appear to be commonest. Clutches of eight have also been recorded in various parts of the bird's range, though it is not clear whether these have been the product of one hen.

Having looked at the general picture of breeding it may now be of interest to examine in detail the history of one clutch. For this I have lumped together observations on different nests in the two study areas. Thus the picture given may be said to be that of the "common" house sparrow (like the "common" man or his equally improbable cousin "the man in the street"). To save constant repetition, I have termed the days of laying as E1, E2, etc.; the day of clutch completion C1 and subsequent days C2, C3 and so on; the day of hatching H1 and the following days up to fledging as H2, H3, etc. in the same way. The statements made are based on slightly over one hundred hours of watching at different nests.

Eggs are normally laid early in the morning. In all of the nests I have examined they have been laid by 0730 G.M.T. In several nests they were laid considerably earlier than this and in one nest examined the first egg of a clutch had already been laid at 0545. Eggs are laid at the rate of one per day.

A certain amount of incubation (or covering of the eggs) takes place after the laying of the first egg; both sexes are involved but the female more than the male. Although the male covers the eggs during the egg-laying period and for a considerable proportion of the time after the clutch is complete (something like thirty-five per cent of the daylight hours as we shall see later), he cannot be said to incubate them as he does not develop incubation patches as does the female. The well insulated nest, together with the covering of the eggs by the male, however, must serve to keep the eggs from chilling during the absences of the female. She is not, or only very rarely, fed by the male when she is on the eggs and must thus spend a considerable time away from the nest obtaining food.

Table 4 gives information on the incubation by both sexes during the egg-laying period; the percentages refer to the waking hours of the birds. During the hours of darkness the female usually roosts in the nest on the eggs; in the day-time the longest spell either bird has been seen in the nest in this period is eight minutes.

TABLE 4

Incubation during the Egg-laying Period

Day	Total time watched min.	Incub. by ♂ min.	%	Incub. by ♀ min.	%	Total Incub. min.	%
E1	61	5·5	9·0	9	14·7	14·5	23·8
E2	74	11	32·4	23	31·1	34	46
E3	86	3	3·5	38·5	44·7	41·5	48
E1–3	221	19·5	9·2	70·5	33·5	90	42·6

The total time spent in watching nests over the egg-laying period is rather small and the percentages given must only be taken as rough indications; nevertheless the table does show that a considerable time is spent on the eggs by both the adults during this stage, though most writers consider that effective incubation does not start until the third egg, at least, is laid and possibly not until the clutch is complete.

Once the clutch is complete the proportion of the day spent in incubation increases rapidly so that, after the fourth day (c5), the adults together spend about 90 per cent of the daylight hours on the eggs. Throughout this time the female still sits on the eggs at night. Table 5 shows the way in which the time spent in sitting varies for the two sexes over the incubation period; the actual time spent in observation for each day is rather small so the results are grouped in two-day periods to give more realistic percentages. The Table shows that the percentage time the female spends in incubation varies little over the incubation period.

TABLE 5
Time Spent in Incubation by the two Sexes

Days	Total time watched (min.)	Incub. by ♂ min.	%	Incub. by ♀ min.	%	Total Incub. min.	%
c1–2	123	19	15·5	73·5	59·7	92·5	75·2
c3–4	136	42	30·9	64·5	47·4	106·5	78·3
c5–6	309	94	30·4	168·5	54·5	262·5	85
c7–8	176	55	31·2	99·5	56·5	154·5	87·7
c9–10	256	117·5	45·9	126·5	49·4	244	95·3
c11–12	183	84	45·7	84	45·7	168	91·8
c13–14	100	31	31	58·5	58·5	89·5	89·5
c15–16	29	6	20·7	20	69	26	89·6
c1–16	1312	448·5	34·2	695	53	1143·5	87·2

On the other hand, the male's enthusiasm for incubation increases slowly and it is not until c9 that the amount of time on the eggs by the male approaches that of the female. As the date of hatching approaches the male seems to become more restless and spends less time in the nest. The average spell spent by either parent on the eggs is about ten minutes; only three spells of above twenty minutes have been recorded (except of course during the night); these were on c2 and c5 for females and on c12 for a male.

Table 6 summarises the records of completed spells by birds of both sexes; these are grouped in three-day periods, starting from clutch completion (c1), in order to obtain meaningful averages. There appears to be little change in the average length of the spell on the eggs as incubation proceeds. The female on the average spends longer periods on the eggs than the male. This agrees with the results in Table 5; a closer analysis suggests that not only are the spells on the eggs by the female longer than those by the male, but also they are more frequent. After the first day or two of incubation the eggs are seldom left uncovered for longer than five

TABLE 6
Lengths of Spells of Incubation

Days	♂				♀			
	Total time (min.)	No. of spells	Average spell (min.)	Max. spell (min.)	Total time (min.)	No. of spells	Average spell (min.)	Max. spell (min.)
c1–3	15	2	7·5	11	49·5	5	9·9	21
c4–6	97·5	10	9·8	18	90	9	10	21
c7–9	89·5	11	8·8	16	111	9	12·3	18
c10–12	125·5	12	10·5	22	129	11	11·7	19
c13–15	29	5	5·8	9	18	2	9	12
c1–15	356·5	40	8·9	22	397·5	36	11·0	21

minutes at a time unless the birds are disturbed or prevented from returning to the nest by the close presence of a human being or cat.

I have only one series of observations on the behaviour of a pair with a completely infertile clutch. The female continued to incubate the eggs for seventeen days (not an abnormally long hatching period). This was a third clutch and was finally deserted on 4th August; perhaps if it had been earlier in the season she would have continued sitting for a longer period. Unfortunately it was not noticed how long the male played his part. Cramp gives the average incubation period of ninety-five clutches as twelve days with a range of nine to eighteen days; his results suggest that it decreases with the advance of the season from an average of 12·4 days in April to 11·3 days in August. Results from twenty-eight clutches in America give a mean of twelve days.

Weaver in his study of the house sparrow at Ithaca, New York, found that the males "were very little in evidence during most of this (the incubation) period and it was rather difficult to determine which males belonged to the various nests." This is quite contrary to all other reported observations on the breeding of house sparrows and appears to be somewhat abnormal, though, as pointed out earlier, the male cannot truly be said to incubate as he does not develop a brood patch.

Coition at the nest is regular during the egg-laying period. It is less frequent once incubation has started but I have recorded it up to c9.

Weaver has given the following most interesting description of hatching. "A clicking sound usually announces the readiness of the young to start hatching. It is made by contact of the egg tooth with the shell and possibly also by a clicking together of the mandibles. The egg tooth presses against the shell and makes an upraised crease around the larger end of the egg about one-fourth of the way from the end. The young bird may break the shell with the egg tooth before the crease is noticeable. In either case, a slit now appears, starting at a point where the egg tooth first pushed through the shell. The slit is made in a circular direction around the egg and meets the point where it started. The young is able to turn itself on its head in the egg making a complete circular slit possible. The head is located in the larger end of the egg and as the slit nears completion the piece of shell around the head is broken off and the head is freed. The larger piece of shell is now kicked free and the young forces itself out. The feet are crowded into the depressions on either side of the neck while in the shell, and after hatching they have a tendency to remain doubled up for several hours. Often the shell does not come free from the young immediately and the female will help to remove it, and when so

PLATE 7. House sparrow nests: *above*, removed from eaves (*D. H. B. Gibbs*); *below*, removed from tree. (*C. W. Teager*)

PLATE 8. House sparrow nests: *above*, nest in nest-box (*R. Hackett*); *below*, nest in ivy. (*C. W. Teager*) A nest-box is usually completely filled. The nest in ivy is an unusually open one

doing may often carry the young and the shell out of the nest causing early death to the unfortunate young."

In my experience most eggs hatch early in the morning, though the hatching period may be spread over two or even three to four days. Presumably this is tied up with the beginning of incubation; if this takes place before the clutch is completed, then a period of forty-eight hours between the first and last hatchings might be expected with the larger clutches. Cramp found that hatching extended beyond twenty-fours in twenty-seven out of ninety-five clutches, though the data available were not sufficient to show that extended hatching periods were significantly more frequent with the larger clutches. During the hatching period the young birds and the remaining eggs are covered almost continuously by one of the adults. In one watch of 120 minutes one or other of the parents was in the nest for 114 minutes being relieved by the other bird when it brought food for the young.

In Table 7 the aggregated results on brooding of young in the nest are analysed for the first eight days of their life. The information for H1 and H2 is given separately and for the eight days in groups of two days to obtain satisfactory percentages. For the first two days of their life the young birds are brooded for just over half of the time. This decreases as the young grow older and it is doubtful if they are brooded much after they are eight days old.

TABLE 7

Brooding of Young

Days	Total time watched (min.)	Brooding by ♂		Brooding by ♀		Total brooding	
		min.	%	min.	%	min.	%
H1	331	97	29·3	85·5	25·8	182·5	55·2
H2	138	41·5	30·1	38·5	27·9	80	58
H1–2	469	138·5	29·5	124	26·4	262·5	56
H3–4	150	16	10·7	20·5	13·6	36·5	24·3
H5–6	182	8·5	4·7	39	21·4	47·5	26·1
H7–8	440	39	8·7	61	13·8	100	22·7

Both of the adults spend spells in the nest after this, but these are mostly short (i.e. less than five minutes compared with ten minutes, which is more typical during the first few days of the life of the young) and may be taken up with feeding the young and encouraging them to defecate. The proportion of time spent in incubation and brooding during daylight hours by the two sexes is indicated in Fig. 14. The female bird usually covers the young during the night right up to the time of fledging; for example, at one nest one of the young fledged on H18 and the two remaining young not until H20—the hen roosted in the nest on the night of H19. D. C. Seel, who observed closely the behaviour of a pair of sparrows with a brood in a nest-box, found a rather higher proportion of brooding: for the first five days the young were brooded for over seventy per cent of the time, thereafter brooding decreased regularly so that by the tenth day it had virtually ceased.

My observations on the feeding of the young in the nest, which are summarised in Table 8, show that this is shared between the sexes, though on balance the female actually brings slightly more food than the male. The distribution of feeding between the sexes varies with the age of the young: for the first few days the male brings food more frequently than his mate; from the sixth or

TABLE 8

Rate of Feeding Young in the Nest

Day	Average rate of feeding (No./hour)			Total time watched (min.)
	♂	♀	Total	
H1–2	5·6	5·5	11·1	556
H3–4	6·6	5·5	12·1	343
H5–6	7·6	6·9	14·5	276
H7–8	7·2	8·6	15·8	668
H9–10	9·0	9·1	18·1	414
H11–12	8·4	9·3	17·7	326
H13–14	8·8	11·0	19·8	422
H15–16	3·1	7·8	10·9	579
H17–18	3·7	10·0	13·7	277
H1–18				3861

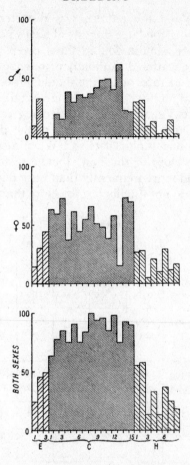

FIG. 14. Percentage of incubation and
brooding in daylight hours.

seventh day after hatching the female's rate exceeds that of the
male, and for the last day or two before the young leave the nest
the male spends considerable periods nearby, calling and displaying
to attract the young from it instead of feeding his family. Seel
found much the same pattern with a pair in Middlesex, the
female's rate exceeding that of the male at the tenth or eleventh

day (at another nest the pattern was distorted by the female disappearing during the later stages); at Seel's nests, however, the feeding rates were almost double those given in Table 8. My observations were scattered randomly throughout the waking day and thus the average rates of feeding should not be unduly upset by any diurnal variation. (Seel's results were obtained from morning watches, when, as I shall show later, feeding rates are generally higher; this explains some but not all of the difference in rate between the two sets of observations.) When a supply of suitable food is available close to the nest, I have watched the parents arriving with food more frequently than once per minute, though spells of this sort do not usually last for more than about a quarter of an hour.

TABLE 9

Diurnal Feeding Rhythm

Hour (G.M.T.)	0500 -0600	0600 -0700	0700 -0800	0800 -0900	0900 -1000	1000 -1100	1100 -1200	1200 -1300
Feeds/hr.	25	22·6	17·6	14·7	15·9	12·1	13·8	7·2
Total time (min.)	55	421	92	200	136	99	147	25

Hour (G.M.T.)	1300 -1400	1400 -1500	1500 -1600	1600 -1700	1700 -1800	1800 -1900	1900 -2000
Feeds/hr.	7·6	5·4	22·2	18·4	11·1	14·3	12·7
Total time (min.)	110	78	75	134	184	92	104

An indication of the variation in the feeding rate throughout the day is given in Table 9 for the days H7–14, during which, according to Table 8, there is little variation in the overall feeding rates. Table 9 includes observations made at times of the year ranging from May until August and does not take into account the variation in daylength over this period. The results are plotted in Fig. 15 (p. 85). It can be seen from this that the feeding rate is at a maximum in the early morning (weakness of the human flesh restricted the amount of observation before 0500) falling to a minimum from 1200–1500; after this another period of intensive feeding takes place with a falling off in the evening. Only at the end of June was feeding after 2000 recorded and too few results were obtained to give a significant feeding rate. Only females were

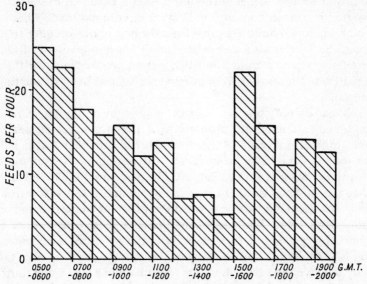

FIG. 15. Diurnal variation in total feeding rate.

seen feeding the young after 2000; at all other times of the year the female of a pair normally goes to roost before her mate, but when there are young in the nest the male goes to roost leaving the female to carry on feeding for as much as half-an-hour before she finally settles down. The latest feed I have seen in Hampshire was at 2020 G.M.T. on 26th June, 1953; this was by a female who then went into the nest to roost.

For the first day after hatching much of the feeding of the young is done by regurgitation (according to Weaver some feeding is done by regurgitation for up to five days) and it is not possible to see what is being brought; later the food can usually be identified before the adult disappears into the nest (Plate 13, p. 132). In the

last few days before fledging the young come to the nest entrance
and the adults feed them there (Plate 14, p. 133). Some idea of the
type of food given to the young may thus be obtained by observation at nests. This shows that the adults tend to concentrate on one
type of food for a period, presumably as the bird is exploiting a
particular source. Much of the insect food is obtained in specially
favoured places; in both my study areas this did not involve flights
of more than two hundred yards from the nest to the foraging area,
though S. Ali reports a case where adult house sparrows in India
were flying up to a mile from their nests to collect food for their
young from bushes that were infested with a plague of defoliating
caterpillars.

As usually only one type of food is brought at any one time a
rough indication of the proportion of the two main classes of
food—animal and vegetable (including bread and other "artificial"
non-protein foods in the latter class)—can be obtained by summing
the number of visits with each type. The percentage of animal food
fed to the young at different ages estimated in this way is shown in
Table 10, also included are results from different workers based on
stomach analyses. The agreement between these observations is
remarkably good and they show how the proportion of animal
food falls rapidly as the chicks grow, so that by the time they are
ready to leave the nest it amounts to probably less than one third;
in a week or two after they leave the nest and become independent
of their parents their diet probably differs in no way from that of
the adult birds.

TABLE 10

Percentage of Animal Food given to Nestlings
at Various Ages

Day	1 2 3 4 5	6 7 8 9	10 11 12	13 14 15
Summers-Smith	←—84—→ ←—67—→	←—50—→	←—40—→	←—33—→
Kalmbach	←—90—→ ←—65—→	←———————49———————→		
Pfeifer	←———100———→		50	20–25
Mansfeld	←—80—→		50	20–25

On the day of hatching, at more than one nest I have seen the parents collecting greenfly and taking them to the nest. As the chicks grow older they are fed on larger soft-bodied insects, such as caterpillars, and later their diet will include tougher food, including beetles, like cockchafers, which are dismembered by the adults before they give them to the young. At the nests I have watched the principal vegetable food brought was bread, though stomach analyses have shown that grain may be fed by the time the young are two or three days old and that by the time they are ready to fledge it may amount to half the food given. No observations on, or stomach analyses of, birds reared in fully built-up surroundings are available but it seems likely that the proportion of animal food given in these circumstances, where insects are less readily available, must be much smaller. It would be interesting to know whether house sparrows can rear their young successfully on an exclusive diet of a vegetable food such as bread.

As the food requirements increase with the growth of the young so the need is met with an increasing amount of vegetable food. Bread (and possibly also grain where it is fed to the young) is usually much more readily obtained than insects, which have to be searched for—I have watched birds collecting bread from within a few yards of a nest and taking it in more frequently than once per minute for short periods and have seen a bird carry up a crust to a gutter beside a nest, break off some small pieces to take in to the young and continue in this way until the crust was finished— whereas visits with insect food are usually separated by several minutes.

Nest sanitation is carried out by both sexes, though both A. J. Berger and Weaver suggest that the female is more assiduous in this than the male. Seel found at one nest that the adults swallowed all the faecal sacs on the first day; on the second day two-thirds, and after that all were carried away. At the nests watched by Seel the young defecated about every two hours; at first the faeces were deposited on the side of the nest, but by the eighth day most were put at the nest entrance and by the twelfth day they were being ejected directly out of the nest.

I have not seen many nestlings leave the nest; the instances I have observed are given in Table 11; also included are some results from a few nests where, although the young were not seen to leave, the time that the nest was empty was noted. All times are G.M.T. It can be seen that most young leave the nest in the morning, sometimes quite early in the morning. In one of the nests

TABLE 11

Departure of Young from the Nest

Date	Brood No.	Remarks
11.7.52	2	All fledged by 1100
28.5.52	1	All fledged by 1330
18.7.53	2	Last young flew at 0748
4.7.53	2	Last young flew at 0635; one had already flown on 2.7.53 and one earlier on 4.7.53
18.6.52	1	One young flew at 0622; two still in nest at 0722 but away by evening
3.8.52	2	Three young watched leaving at 1121, 1350 and 1507; nest then empty
6.6.53	1	Last young flew at 0915
17.8.53	1	All fledged by 1100

where the whole brood was seen leaving the nest there was a spread of almost four hours between the first and third (last). In one of the others one young left the nest two days before the remainder, though this is not surprising in a species which begins incubation with the first egg or at least before the clutch is complete and where the period of hatching can extend over three or four days. When the young leave like this on different days or separated by some hours the parents usually split duties, one feeding the young in the nest, the other the fledglings. After the rather prolonged nestling period for a bird of this size, the young are strong on the wing when they leave the nest. The difficulty of obtaining exact information on the time of fledging for the house sparrow is complicated by the fact that young birds may return to the nest after they have "fledged". I have suspected this on a number of occasions and finally got proof at a nest in a nest-box in 1953. All the young had flown by 0635 on 4th July; however, at 0600 on 5th July a young bird was again calling from the nest entrance, though as far as could be seen it was not fed again there by its parents. Cramp gives the mean nestling period in Great Britain as 14·4 days with a range of eleven to nineteen days. Weaver obtained precisely the same mean for twenty-three broods in the U.S.A.

The death of one of the parents may cause the other to desert but only, in my experience, if the young birds are recently hatched. At one nest the male died on H3 and the female deserted. She subsequently obtained another mate and reared two broods with him. On the other hand, at a nest where the male died on H11, the female continued to feed the young and reared them successfully. Similarly at another nest, where the female disappeared about H5, the male continued to feed the young, though he also died (on H14), not through overwork but by getting his legs entangled in the horsehair lining of the nest. H. Brackbill informs me that a hen deserted her nest on being ringed when the young were twelve days old; the male then also left the nestlings and they died. This may have been the result of interference or merely the sort of difference in behaviour that can be expected between individuals. The pair subsequently returned to the nest and reared a second brood. I have four records of adults deserting nests and subsequently rearing further broods. One pair deserted an incomplete clutch of three eggs on 24th May and finally started a second clutch on 7th July in a different nest, after having prospected several other sites. The young in this nest hatched but two died on 1st August and the last on 3rd August; this nestling was fed up to the end by the female and it does not seem that the death of the brood was the result of lack of food. At another nest, four of a clutch of five hatched on 5th July (the fifth egg was infertile). The young birds were dead in the nest on 9th July; whether they died from lack of attention or from other causes was not known, though this pair started another clutch in the same nest on 20th July. These eggs hatched on 2nd August but the young were dead in the nest on 12th August. Both of the parents were still alive on this date.

Young that die in the nest are removed by the male and dropped on the ground nearby. During the breeding season a number of unfledged and partially fledged young may be found on the ground in a breeding colony. For instance, on 1st August, 1953, I found three such dead young; two were ejected from one nest at 1310 and at 1510 G.M.T. (they were then ten days old), the other, then three days old, came from another nest at 1345. In two nests where the female has died I have known the male to stop feeding the young and then after they have died to remove the corpses from the nest preparatory to attempting to obtain another mate. Infertile eggs do not appear to be removed.

Many observers have remarked on the number of naked young that can be found dead on the ground near the nests. These could merely be dismissed as dead nestlings that have been removed from nests but for some remarkable observations made by A. H. Scott on captive house sparrows. Scott bred house sparrows for a number of years in a large planted aviary. He ringed a brood of four young sparrows one day but they were rather young and he was doubtful whether the rings would stay on. When he went to check this the following day there was only one nestling in the nest. Further examination revealed that two of the nestlings were in another sparrow's nest about twenty-four feet away with two young birds that had previously been in that nest. The fourth young was found dead on the ground between the nests. The two young were taken over and reared by their foster parents. Scott is of the opinion that the adults had carried the young across after their nest had been disturbed. He was actually present in the aviary when the hen at the same nest dropped a live nestling of a subsequent brood when attempting to carry it across the aviary towards an unoccupied nest-box. Again this took place after he had just disturbed the nest by ringing the young. Scott reports other similar occurrences in his aviary. Captive birds may well behave abnormally but Scott also found young sparrows on the ground outside free-living house sparrows' nests after he had disturbed the chicks, though he did not see them being carried by the adults. He suggests that the house sparrow may be evolving from the lowest stage of parental behaviour (desertion) to a higher stage of activity—saving the young by attempting to remove them to an undisturbed nest. I know of no other evidence to support this hypothesis but it certainly suggests a most interesting field of investigation.

A most unusual case of faithfulness to the young in the nest is given by A. W. Boyd. On 22nd May, 1930 a nest was pulled out of a roof and thrown on to a midden; it had not been realised that it contained young, but the old birds followed it and for two days were seen feeding the young where the nest had been thrown. Even when there has been a considerable amount of interference at the nest, the birds rarely desert their young. Individuals vary somewhat in their reaction to an intruder; some of my colour-ringed birds would continue to feed their young even when I was a few feet away from the nest, others would not go in if I was in sight and watching them, though they were not put off if I was working nearby and not looking at them. This consciousness of being observed is interesting and there is no doubt that the birds in my study colonies became much more wary than those that were not regularly watched.

Another interesting observation of attachment of parents to their young was given me by Major A. C. Booth. Here a pair of sparrows was seen regularly flying up to the ventilation grilles situated in the walls of a house about a foot above the ground over a period of three days; investigation showed that they were feeding through the grille a young sparrow that had fallen down the cavity wall. A hole was made in one of the grilles and the young bird came out and flew away strongly with the adults—it had obviously fledged a few days previously. The surprising thing is that the parents had been able to locate it through the grille and had not deserted it when it would not follow them. An even more extra-ordinary case of attachment of parents to their young is quoted by Yarrell: "It is stated that a few years since a pair of sparrows, which had built in a thatch roof of a house at Poole, was observed to continue their regular visits to the nest long after the time when the young birds take flight. This unusual circumstance continued throughout the year; and in the winter, a gentleman who had all along observed them, determined on investigating its cause. He therefore mounted a ladder, and found one of the young ones detained a prisoner, by means of a piece of string or worsted, which formed part of the nest, having become accidentally twisted round its leg. Being thus incapacited for procuring its own sustenance, it had been fed by the continued exertions of its parents." String and hair in the nest seem to be a regular hazard. I have seen birds entangled in this way several times and a case has been reported of an adult hen having one of her unfledged young attached to her by a piece of string so that she became exhausted and was killed by a dog; the nestling was still alive.

The hatching and fledging success based on the analysis of the British Trust for Ornithology records are summarised in Table 12. The estimation of breeding success from data obtained from Nest Record Cards is subject to various errors, such as observer bias and the effect of nest-finding on the subsequent success as well as faults inherent in the analysis, which tend to render the figures for hatching success rather optimistic and those for fledging success rather pessimistic. The results, however, are of interest for comparison with those of other species obtained in the same way and also among themselves. It appears that the chance of eggs hatching

TABLE 12

Breeding Success

Clutch completed	Eggs laid	Eggs hatched No.	%	Eggs hatched	Young fledged No.	%	Breeding success
Mar./Apr.	507	359	71	276	217	79	56
May	1202	820	68	571	454	80	54
June	673	501	74	354	251	71	53
Jul./Aug.	392	300	77	200	122	63	49
Total	2774	1980	71	1401	1044	74	53

increases during the breeding season, whereas fledging success increases to a maximum for nestlings from clutches laid in May and then decreases. It is difficult to speculate why hatching success should change in this way without more information on the reasons why eggs fail, though, in a hole-nesting species like the sparrow, predation is not likely to be of importance and the most probable causes of failure are infertility and chilling, the latter presumably being more probable early in the season. The decrease in fledging success in the latter part of the season could be a result of difficulty in the adults finding suitable food for the young or a recession in the breeding drive. The overall success of just over fifty per cent is surprisingly small for a hole-nesting species—Mrs. M. M. Nice, in a recent analysis of the published information on breeding success of altricial (nidicolous) birds, found hole-nesters averaged sixty-six per cent success, whereas with open-nesters it was only forty-six per cent. The main reason for the difference in the success of the house sparrow compared with the hole-nesters summarised by Mrs. Nice lies in fledging success rather than in hatching success and it could be that the house sparrow by continuing to use the same nest for subsequent broods and from year to year suffers more from the effect of nest parasites than other hole-nesters, which are not attached to one nest hole to the same extent. This effect would become more pronounced as the time of occupancy during the season increases and could account for the decrease in fledging success towards the end of the summer. Two sets of American results, though admittedly on very small samples, gave rather higher values: Weaver, seventy-one per cent of a hundred and eighty eggs, and W. L. McAtee, eighty-three per cent of a hundred and seventeen eggs. Using the British results, a pair can expect on average to produce four to five fledged young per year.

Young sparrows, like the young of most nidicolous species, are not able to feed themselves when they leave the nest. Observations on captive birds show that they begin to pick up food at about seven days after leaving the nest, though they may be fed by their parents for up to fourteen days after fledging. When it is realised that the period from the start of egg laying to fledging takes about a month and that many pairs have three broods, it is inevitable that the broods must follow each other in rapid succession. On the average the interval between fledging of one brood and the beginning of egg laying of the next is nine or ten days. On numerous occasions I have found this period to be as short as four or five days and there are even reports from America of eggs of another clutch being laid in a nest before the young of the previous brood have flown. In cases like this it is clear that the cock must still be looking after the young of one brood while the hen is making a start with the next one. Indeed observations show that feeding of young birds out of the nest is much more commonly done by the cock than by the hen. This behaviour provides further evidence of individual recognition because during the period the young are still being fed by their parents the latter leave them from time to time to attend to the start of the next clutch; yet they appear to be able to find them again quite easily.

During the period immediately after fledging the parents are still much attached to their young and if one of these is trapped the adult bird remains close by, calling when the young bird is being handled and ringed.

CHAPTER 9

GROWTH AND DEVELOPMENT

R. L. WEAVER studied the growth of nestling house sparrows by examining daily the young in a large number of nest-boxes. I have hand-reared nestlings from three days old and have also watched the development of young birds born in an aviary. From these studies we can obtain a fairly complete picture of this stage in the life of the bird.

Young house sparrows are born without down; the feather tracts are visible beneath the skin, though the feathers themselves do not begin to sprout until the fourth day, when all the feather tracts are clearly to be seen. From birth they react to noise and vibration by thrusting their bills up vertically; although the eyes open on the fifth day, it was about another twenty-four hours before the hand-reared birds were directing their bills towards the food I offered. By the seventh day, feathers are breaking through from all the tracts and from this stage on feathering proceeds rapidly and the birds can be recognised as young sparrows.

Weaver's results for wing length and weight are given in Fig. 16 (p. 96). It can be seen that the growth rates are remarkably uniform, though the rate of increase in weight begins to slow down about the tenth or eleventh day, and the birds leave the nest when they weigh approximately twenty-five grammes. There is definitely a slowing down in the rate of feeding as the young approach fledging and there is probably a fall in weight for the first day or two after they leave the nest; the average weight of full-grown house sparrows is about twenty-eight grammes. After the third day the wing grows steadily without a check at the time of fledging; the average wing length of adult house sparrows in Great Britain (taking both sexes together) is about seventy-five millimetres but I think this is seldom attained by the birds in their first plumage; fifty birds in juvenile plumage that I measured averaged only 72·5 millimetres with a range of sixty-nine to seventy-seven millimetres. The birds can fly

when the wing length is about fifty millimetres; some young leave
the nest before this and though they can glide and reach the
ground without mishap it appears that they are unable to gain
height. These birds are enticed under cover by their parents and
may survive until they can fly properly. One such young I saw
landing in the centre of a road with a certain amount of traffic
passing along; the hen flew down with food and began to entice

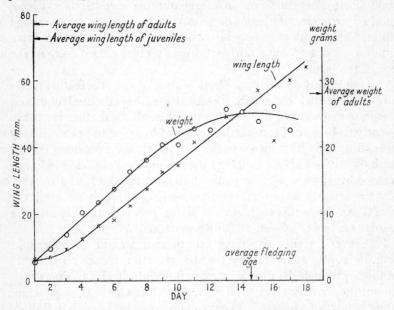

FIG. 16. Development of nestling house sparrows. (After R. L. Weaver.)

the fledgling to the side, flying away each time a car came along
and returning when it had passed. Miraculously the young bird
escaped being flattened, though cars passed over it, reached the
gutter and eventually, by following the hen, the safety of a hedge
where it was at last given food. It remained there while the hen
continued feeding it; on one occasion a cat passed within two feet
without noticing it.

Young birds that can fly follow their parents around clammer-
ing for food. When young birds leave the nest normally (i.e. without

PLATE 9. Female at entrance to nest in tree hole, a site not commonly used by house sparrows in Great Britain. (*M. S. Wood*)

PLATE 10. Nest in nest-box. Large numbers of feathers are used to line the nest. (*E. Hosking*)

leaving because they have been disturbed) at fourteen to fifteen days, they can fly strongly. Weaver has suggested that the brood splits up between the parents; I have not found this and in my experience it is usually the male that feeds them out of the nest, the female soon making a start with a new brood. Possibly the splitting of the brood may occur in those nests in which about half of the young fledge one day and the remainder the next.

When the young leave the nest their plumage is very similar to that of the adult female, though they tend to be somewhat paler. At first they can be fairly readily distinguished by the much more conspicuous yellowish hinge to the bill, by the rather thicker and smoother tarsus (in the adult the latter has a dried, more withered appearance) and a generally more "babyish" look (Plate 15, p.140). Very soon, however, they are difficult to separate, though, of course, if the bird is handled it can be seen that the feathers of the adults at this time of year are abraded while those of the young birds are perfect. Four to six weeks after they leave the nest the moulting of the juvenile plumage begins but it is another four weeks before the males begin to show the first definite signs of their sex, the chestnut patch on the scapulars; the first signs of the black throat appear in the next week and finally the head pattern. The moult in the juvenile is complete and includes wing and tail.

First-year birds can still be distinguished for some time by the different appearance of the legs, but in the late autumn and the winter separation of young and adult live birds becomes more and more difficult, though in dead specimens the first-year birds can still be distinguished by the degree of ossification of the skull; R. W. Nero has shown that in house sparrows pneumatisation is not complete until the birds are thirty-one to thirty-two weeks old. J. Davis and B. S. Davis by examination of birds taken in California, were able to show that some young males with incomplete ossification were in full breeding condition in June and July—the testes had enlarged and the bill was blackened—although only traces of adult plumage were apparent. The normal breeding season of the house sparrow in southern California begins in March but it is suggested that these birds may well have come from out-of-season clutches laid earlier in the year, though if this were the case why should the moult have been delayed? It is of interest that the male of a pair of birds that were taken after being seen copulating in India in November had still an incompletely ossified skull; the female of the pair had a prominent brood patch, suggesting that in fact the birds were breeding. Another male with a nest taken in April had also an unossified patch in the centre of its skull; this bird must have been born in the autumn.

These observations suggest an explanation for the out-of-season breeding that is not infrequently recorded for the species and also suggest that birds of the year may be sufficiently mature in the autumn to provide some of the replacement mates for broken pairs. G. M. Riley by means of photostimulation experiments showed that, whereas adult males that had bred earlier in the year showed no response to an artificial increase in the hours of light starting in September, birds of the year showed a marked sexual development; by the middle of November, however, the refractory period in the adults was over and they began to respond to artificially increasing daylength. It seems probable that the increase in the number of displays in late September and October, as shown in Fig. 8, p. 61, is related to sexual development of young males. In the wild, adult male sparrows show a sexual recrudescence in November; this is followed by a temporary regression in the middle of the winter. In normal circumstances no sexual development of the females occurs in the autumn.

H. Löhrl and R. Böhringer, who examined a large series of house sparrows poisoned in November and December in Germany, found on the average that the birds of the year were slightly over half a gramme lighter than the adults, so that some difference must persist up to the end of the year. In the same way the wing length of the young birds was on the average 0·7 to 1 millimetre shorter. Some of these first-year birds as well as a few of the adult males, had completely black bills in November.

Claims have been made that the sexes can be differentiated while the birds are still in juvenile plumage. For instance, it has been suggested that young males show some signs of a darker bib and that a white spot is evident behind the eye of the male but not of the female (see the right-hand bird in Plate 15, p. 140); in my view, however, neither of these are reliable characteristics. Recently H. L. Secker in New Zealand has suggested to me that the under-tail coverts are medium-brown in the female but white, or at the most light-brown, in the male and he considers that by taking this characteristic in conjunction with the bib colour sexing is possible. Further work is needed to establish this and the method obviously requires a good deal of experience in handling young sparrows. I noticed an interesting feature in young birds reared in my aviary: when the nestlings were about twelve days old there were two distinct plumage types—one very similar to the hen, the other much brighter with a clear buff stripe leading back from the eye, light cheeks and chin, and a dark throat. Within a day or two of leaving the nest the brighter colouration faded and the types could no longer be distinguished. J. T. Nichols trapped very similarly plumaged juveniles in the U.S.A. These brighter birds were very probably males but whether all males are distinguished in this way at this stage requires further investigation.

Plumage variants are also noticeable among the adults. One of the commonest features is the appearance of chestnut-brown replacing black in the male; this is most frequent in the bib, which may be completely chestnut, though it occasionally occurs in the head feathers resulting in birds resembling the clearly marked sub-species *italiae*. In six thousand males examined by R. Piechocki 3·5 per cent showed some signs of chestnut. In some hens, signs of a blackish bib can be detected. A. Hazelwood and E. Gorton have reported a variant population in Devonshire; in both sexes there was a strong suffusion of wheaten-yellow over the underparts and the breeding plumage in the males was much reduced. White, albino, black and numerous other plumage variants are reported from time to time.

An indication of the seasonal development of the bird is given by the colour of the male's bill: in the breeding season it is black, in the non-breeding season horn. W. N. Keck showed that the change from horn to black is controlled by hormones and it can be taken as an indicator of the development of the gonads. In European and American populations, where breeding does not normally begin until April, isolated individuals have been noticed with black bills as early as December and a significant proportion are thus distinguished by the end of January. This early development is in line with the marked increase in the number of displays that begins in the second half of January as shown in Fig. 8, p. 61. The reversion to horn colour begins in the summer months; though C. B. Ticehurst and R. E. Cheesman reported that the race occurring in central and eastern Arabia (sub. sp. *hufufae*) retained their black bills throughout the year. The annual moult of the adults may occur from late June to early November in Britain, though it is mainly in the period July to mid-October.

A further change that occurs in the male as the breeding season approaches is an increase in the extent of the black bib. The breast feathers, which are renewed at the moult, have black bases but grey tips; during the winter gradual abrasion of the light tip takes place exposing more of the black portion of the feather and causing an extension of the black area in the spring. (Compare the spring plumaged male in Plate 1, p. 32, with the autumn bird in Plate 3a, p. 48.)

Developments in behaviour are also of interest. Even at eight to ten days old the nestlings begin to deposit their faeces away from the nest cup, and in nests where the entrance is sufficiently close to the cup they will begin to eject their faeces out of the nest some days before they are ready to leave. At six days they begin to preen and by nine days they exercise their wings and flap and shiver them when soliciting for food. At this stage I found that hand-reared birds began to show signs of shyness and attempted to hide themselves once their immediate hunger had been satisfied. Before this they had continued to beg for food even after they were incapable of swallowing any more.

When they leave the nest the young birds solicit food from any adult sparrow by calling and shivering their wings (Plate 16, p. 141). The birds I had reared and released in an aviary solicited food from passing human beings, though they were torn between the desire for food and their obvious fear, but not from adult sparrows. Very soon after leaving the nest they attempted to pick up food but I do not think that they were able to feed themselves for about a week after they had fledged; a few days after this they would no longer accept food from me. The fledglings were first seen drinking on the tenth day and bathing on the fifteenth day.

In this period of early life precocious reproductive behaviour may be seen. F. L. Hudson reported newly fledged sparrows breaking off dead grass and taking it into some bushes; my aviary fledglings carried grass into nest-boxes and I have seen young, still being fed by their parents, taking grass into the roost at night. Hudson also saw a recently fledged bird pecking the cloaca of a female, as in the communal display, and I have several times seen attempted coition by young birds only two to three weeks out of the nest. At this age sexual behaviour is only at low intensity; it dies away almost completely at about four or five weeks and does not re-appear until the birds are pretty well adult.

Another odd thing I noticed with my young captive birds was the development of a song—this was a sustained, rambling warbling, reminiscent of a goldfinch or linnet, built up of the adult chirrup notes but much more musical than normally associated with the house sparrow. Like the other activities described above it lasted only a week or two when the birds had been flying for about a month. It is not, however, confined to birds brought up in an artificial environment for I have from time to time heard similar songs from fully wild birds (even as late as November), though I have no information on the age of any of them, and H. Sick has reported singing of "female-coloured" young birds in Brazil. It is interesting that Clarence, the hero of Clare Kipps's "Sold for a Farthing", developed a song, much more complex than the normal sparrow utterings, when he was about six months old and retained this song for the rest of his life. House sparrows reared by themselves in captivity are said to develop a melodious song quite different from the harsh utterings of their wild relatives.

CHAPTER 10

COLONIAL AND SOCIAL BEHAVIOUR

THE house sparrow over most of its range is very closely associated with man. Nests are usually on buildings, either in holes under roofs or in creepers, less frequently in the branches of trees and rather seldom in holes in trees. When tree sites are used these are invariably close to buildings, very rarely more than a hundred yards away. This restriction of breeding habitat inevitably leads to some concentration of the birds. However, closer study reveals that not all of the available breeding habitat is used, the birds tending to concentrate into discreet breeding colonies so that some suitable breeding places are not occupied.

Fig. 17, opposite, shows an area of some two square miles in Hampshire. This was carefully surveyed in 1952 and 1953 and all houses examined to see whether they were used by house sparrows for breeding (nests in trees were considered as being on the nearest house). Houses having nests are blocked in on the Figure. It will be seen that these amount to only about twenty-five per cent of the total and that they tend to be concentrated in small groups; these colonies are indicated by broken circles and it is believed that during the breeding season little, if any, interchange of adult sparrows took place between them, the foraging area of Colony 1 being within a radius of a hundred to a hundred and fifty yards. Birds from different colonies might resort to some particularly favoured feeding spot to collect food for their young; these places, however, lay outside the colony area and birds of one colony did not forage in another colony's breeding area. For example, the point marked A in the Figure was a rather marshy area and was much used by birds from the neighbouring Colonies 1, 2 and 3, particularly at the beginning of the breeding season when there was a flush of insects available to house sparrows in the rushes and long grass; presumably at this time insects of the type collected by sparrows were not as easily obtainable elsewhere. W. Haller had

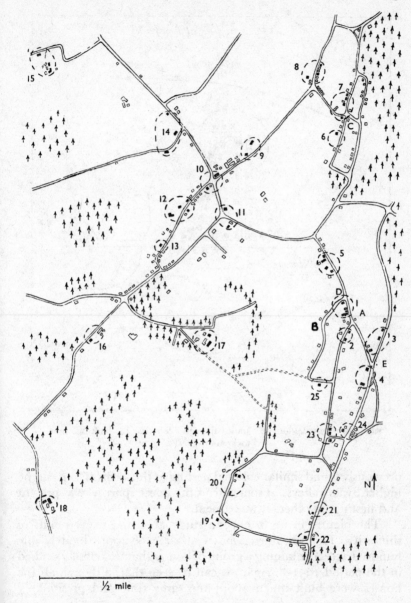

FIG. 17. Distribution of house sparrow colonies in rural area in Hampshire.

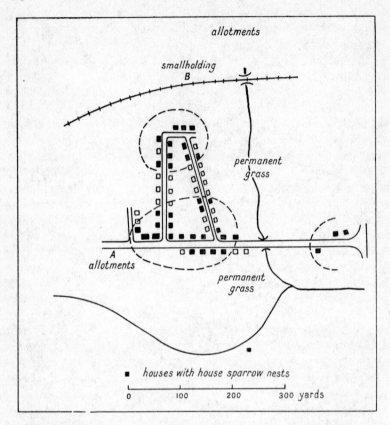

allotments

smallholding
B

permanent
grass

A
allotments

permanent
grass

■ houses with house sparrow nests

0   100   200   300 yards

FIG. 18. Distribution of house sparrow colonies in built-up area, Stockton-on-Tees.

previously found similar colonial nesting at the farms of some of the higher Swiss valleys; at some farms the house sparrow was present and nesting, at others it was absent.

The picture in my suburban study area had many points of similarity. Fig. 18, above, shows an area of approximately one hundred acres containing a group of houses that was closely studied in the period 1954–8. Again it can be seen that, although all the houses were built much about the same time and presumably offered the same nesting opportunities to the sparrows, the breeding birds tended to collect into small colonies, some of the houses in the colony area having as many as six nests. Each year young cocks would adopt nest sites on the houses bordering the colony and call at them to attract a mate, but they were normally unsuccessful in this, the hens preferring to pair with cocks that had nests in the colony area. One major difference between the rural and the suburban area was the much greater density of house sparrows in the latter. The result of this was that the colonies were much less discreet and much more trespassing between them took place. In fact it is doubtful if the individual colonies were sufficiently separated to merit this name.

As in the rural area particularly favoured foraging places would draw adults when collecting food for their young. One such area was in the allotments at the point A in the Figure, which attracted birds from up to three hundred yards; another area was a hen run (marked B) which was visited by birds nesting five hundred yards away. With the much greater density of breeding birds, there was considerable foraging by the birds of one colony in the breeding areas of neighbouring colonies.

A similar social organisation of the house sparrow population of Kiel has been described by Fräulein M. Fallet, though she prefers to restrict the use of the term "colony" to those groups of birds nesting side by side in ivy or in a tree, using the term *Aktionsgemeinschaft* (action community) for the less closely associated group of nesting birds that I describe as a colony. Possibly the social bond in Fallet's colonies is stronger than in her *Aktionsgemeinschäften*, though I think the difference is one of degree rather than of kind; the members of these colonies, which roost together and indulge in pre-roosting and post-roosting social song, as do other communally roosting sparrows, formed about nine per cent of the Kiel house sparrow population. There is a strong tendency for house sparrows to form these closely associated nesting colonies when the conditions permit, but usually lack of nesting opportunities forces them to form more scattered, though still socially connected, communities.

The advantages of colonial nesting to a species like the house sparrow are not obvious. In open nesting species like the gulls and terns, colonial breeding provides protection against predators and together with synchronisation of breeding, which means that a shorter period is available for the predators to prey on the eggs and young, results in decreased mortality during the vulnerable period in the nest. The house sparrow, on the other hand, is not subject to any great degree of predation while in the nest and hence colonial nesting can have little advantage in this respect. Social behaviour gives a clear advantage in such extra-breeding activities as feeding and bathing, where an alarm by one bird can alert the whole group. Possibly this is the reason for social behaviour in the house sparrow and has led to colonial nesting. The method of pair formation described in an earlier chapter would tend to maintain such a colony once formed. Provided not positively disadvantageous to the species, colonial behaviour would have thus become the rule. It follows naturally from the choice of a restricted breeding habitat —man's habitations—and the general behaviour and method of pair formation in the species. It should be noted also that there is a strong tendency for social breeding in all of the weaver-birds, most of which do not necessarily breed close to man's dwellings. In general there are two distinct groups of socially breeding birds: strong flying species that are able to range over a wide area to obtain food but are concentrated for breeding by the shortage of suitable, safe nesting sites; the other group consists of species attracted by a concentrated supply of food and able to nest in close proximity to it. In the former group we find the colonial nesting sea-birds and passerines like the rook and sand martin; in the latter we get the house sparrow and tropical weaver-birds.

The behaviour of the birds flocking in the grain fields is particularly interesting: unlike the yellowhammers and greenfinches, which tend to feed in the centre of the field well away from the edges, the sparrows like to operate from a thick hedge or other vantage point, seldom venturing in more than five yards from the edge. In this way a band of this width round the field can be almost completely stripped; where there is a large flock the stalks in this strip get broken down and the grain that is not eaten gets shaken from the ears as it ripens (Plate 17, p. 176). The birds do not feed randomly but behave socially as a flock. They feed together in a tight group and if one bird gives the alarm "quer quer" the whole party makes for the safety of the hedge; the reverse process back to the grain starts with a trickle of one or two birds and then, if there is no further alarm, the whole assembly cascades out again. It is obvious that this behaviour is advantageous in that imminent danger is almost certainly detected by odd birds in the feeding flock and the whole can quickly attain the protection of the hedge. On the other hand it has its disadvantages when a large number is present: so many warnings against real or imagined danger are given by individual birds that the time available for feeding is severely reduced. The flock continues to feed in this way for some time and then suddenly the birds move off without warning to another part of the field; sometimes they stop feeding and sit together in the hedge preening and singing socially or, if there is water nearby, they may begin bathing. Again one is struck by the strong social bond that exists in the flock, the individuals adopting the same activity. The way in which this is achieved is puzzling. Are there dominant individuals in the group that set the pace or in a social group does a desire to indulge in certain activities arise in a majority of the individuals at the same time? In winter much food seeking is also done communally and the birds gather together in some favoured spot and indulge in social singing in a nearby hedge or tree after they have fed (Plate 18, p. 177). In many ways this is reminiscent of the feeding behaviour in the fields: the birds all chirp away together until one gives an alarm call and silence falls; after a short interval one bird begins to call again and soon the whole flock is calling together once more.

Roosting is at times a social activity with the house sparrow and communal roosts may be formed. There is, however, considerable variation in the roosting behaviour, not only with the season but also with the latitude and also among different individuals. I shall describe what I consider to be the most general roosting pattern and then we can see how this is altered to meet different circumstances. As we have already seen when the young birds leave their nests and become independent of their parents they collect together in flocks at suitable feeding places; these flocks grow in size as the season advances, finally gravitating to the ripening grain fields. The birds tend to remain together during the day and at night they roost communally in a thick hedge or other cover, if possible beside the feeding area, though if necessary they will move a mile or two to find a suitable place should a nearer one not be available; the numbers roosting together increase as the season advances and at times may amount to many thousands. When the adults have finished with their breeding duties they join the feeding flocks and some join the communal roosts at night, but if they are not too far away from their breeding area they may return instead to their nests. When the grain has been harvested the birds return to their breeding areas and although communal roosts may be formed in these in bushes, creepers or trees, I think the birds prefer secure holes in buildings and thus where these are plentiful the social roosts that are formed in the breeding areas at the beginning of the autumn are gradually given up. Small groups may use the same entrance hole under the eaves of a house and the nests may be used by one or both of the pair that bred in them during the previous summer. It was these birds that Browning was referring to when he wrote:

> Hark 'tis the sparrow's good-night twitter
> about your cottage eaves.

On the other hand where holes are in short supply, as they apparently were in my rural study colony, a communal roost may be maintained throughout the year except during the brief period of exodus to the grain fields. The communal sites in the breeding areas tend to be traditional and are used from year to year; whereas the summer roosts are not only changed from time to time during the summer as the foraging flocks change their feeding areas but also different sites are used each year. The communal roost used by my Hampshire birds was in a thick overgrown privet hedge on the edge of the colony area; the birds using it were for the most part immatures that had not yet adopted nesting sites, though a number of adults used it throughout their lives. Although the females particularly tended to roost in their nests at night, they were somewhat erratic in this—sometimes roosting in their nest and at other times joining the communal roost. It is possible that on some nights as a result of disturbance near the nests at roosting time the birds were reluctant to enter them. On the other hand in the suburban colony, where there was no communal roost, the behaviour was much more consistent and if there was some disturbance near the nest site the birds would hang around well beyond their normal roosting time until the coast was clear and they could go in without fear. Here small roosts were formed in the breeding areas on the return from the grain fields but the birds soon deserted these and adopted holes in the eaves of houses, sometimes sharing these with other sparrows and starlings.

While there are eggs or young in the nest these are almost invariably covered at night by the hen. When the young fledge the family may roost together for a few nights if a lot of cover is available near the nest or they may be taken directly to a communal roost in the breeding colony area. When the female lays a subsequent clutch she at once reverts to her original habit of roosting in the nest, though the cock continues to roost with his young until they become independent. There is usually an outburst of feeding just before the birds settle down and in the summer months adults can frequently be seen feeding their recently fledged young beside the roost before the family retires for the night.

I think that roosting behaviour in the winter is also affected by climate, communal roosts becoming more frequent further south in the bird's range in the northern hemisphere. In higher latitudes with severe winters, hole roosting becomes almost obligatory and the use of "roost nests" becomes much more common.

Thus we have alternative solutions to the same problem: where holes in buildings are plentiful they are adopted in preference, and there are frequent reports of birds roosting in unusual sites, such as the inside of street lamps; where holes are scarce a communal roost is formed in some site where the birds have security and protection from the weather. There is a tendency as the winter advances for roosts in creepers and trees to be given up for holes— presumably this occurs as the birds locate suitable holes during their nest-site prospecting activities—which are used in preference to the more open sites that become increasingly exposed as the leaves drop. Where there is a high density of sparrows, suitable roosting places may be difficult to find and there are numerous reports of large roosts in plane trees in London, and many other cities on the Continent, where the birds are rather exposed. There are several records of birds being washed out of such sites in severe rain or hail storms and being drowned or beaten to death; for example, two hundred birds were drowned at one roost in Bethnal Green in London in 1867, "several hundred" were killed on the night of 11th November, 1887, at a roost in Washington, D.C. during a severe thunderstorm and "basketfuls" were picked up below a roost in Nîmes after a night of heavy hail and thunder in 1920.

Some of the temporary summer roosts may reach very large proportions, though nothing like the number of starlings to be found in their winter roosts. I am indebted to C. Harrison for details of a very large roosting concentration that formed in the late summer of 1949 on the outskirts of South London (on 29th August it was estimated that approximately nineteen thousand birds were present); this roost was typical of ones formed in the summer in that it was occupied only for a short period and was not used in subsequent years. One of the most interesting features of Harrison's observations was that the birds tended to converge on the roost—in flocks of up to about one thousand birds—from one direction, following definite flight lines; these were by no means direct and the birds followed hedges and lines of trees or kept close to houses in preference to shorter routes across open land. On 29th August, when a count was made, birds were arriving at the roost from 16.00 to 17.34 G.M.T. (sunset 17.41); at the peak, which lasted for seven minutes from 16.25, it was estimated that approximately six hundred birds were arriving per minute—as Harrison describes it: "For the next seven minutes birds poured in in a continuous stream, the sky appeared to rain sparrows as each flock scattered over the area and individual birds swooped down." R. E. Moreau recorded a late summer roost of house sparrows in Egypt, which at its peak probably contained one hundred thousand birds. These enormous concentrations are clearly associated with a locally plentiful supply of food; in the case of the Egyptian birds this was provided by the roofless store houses which were heaped with boatloads of grain brought down the Nile. However, the strong social pull of roosting behaviour is shown by the fact that some of these birds were being drawn from up to four miles away; to some extent the formation of a very large roost in Egypt can be explained by the general shortage of suitable roosting trees but many of these birds were coming from areas where there were trees so that there was still an over-riding social effect. A sparrow-hawk appeared at the roost in the middle of October (sparrow-hawks are only winter visitors to Egypt); the first effect was to disperse the birds over a wide area of the trees but within a few nights the whole roosting concentration had been broken up by the single predator. Numbers at winter roosts are much smaller; a large one that was used in the 1930's in Richmond Park served two thousand to three thousand birds.

Both barn and tawny owls visit sparrow roosts at night and judging by the number of rings placed on house sparrows that are subsequently found in pellets, seem to have some success there. P. A. Rayfield has told me how in one of the Naval Stores in England the number of sparrows nesting and roosting on rafters inside the buildings was causing a considerable nuisance; measures were taken against the sparrows but the problem remained until a tawny owl took to roosting in one of the buildings during the day and feeding on the sparrows at night. This considerably reduced the sparrow numbers, which were then held in check after the owl had moved on, by structural alterations to the buildings. Since then a sparrow-hawk spent some time in one of the buildings living right on top of an easy source of food despite the efforts of the workmen to drive it away. It would appear that the advantages to be gained from this social behaviour are sufficient to outweigh the disadvantages of a predator settling down at one of these communal sites and making severe depredations on the birds.

The behaviour at roosting time is very striking and has been remarked by a number of writers. Birds arrive at their roosting place early enough but seem reluctant to settle for the night. Where there is a communal roost the first individuals may turn up more than an hour before the birds finally quieten down. These early

birds call beside the roost and are very restless, disputes regularly
breaking out; alarm calls and tail flicking are frequent, suggesting
that the birds are in a state of nervous tension. With each fresh
arrival excitement breaks out anew; at times a party will fly out
from the hedge and indulge in aerial evolutions before returning to
the site. P. E. Parry, for instance, describes a roost of three hundred
to four hundred house sparrows in thick ivy on a stone wall in
Cambridge; in the pre-roosting period, flocks of five to one
hundred birds would fly round for up to ten minutes like a
flock of starlings before finally settling down in the ivy.

A most graphic description of house sparrows arriving at a
roost in trees in the centre of Boston, U.S.A., on 20th November,
1906, is given by C. W. Townsend. Sunset on that day was at 5.24
p.m.; the first birds arrived at the roosting trees at 3.45 and by 4.10
there were "now about one hundred and fifty sparrows present, but
new ones are constantly sailing in with wings spread from over or
between the surrounding high buildings. They fly with astonishing
swiftness and directness, projected as it were from space directly
into the roost." At 4.15 Townsend goes on to say: "It is now raining
birds. The trees are a scene of great activity and the noise rises above
the roar of the city's streets. The birds are crowding together in the
trees, constantly fighting and flying about as they are forced from
their perches." This stream of arrivals continued until 4.45 when
the numbers began to fall off and movement had ceased by 5.0 p.m.

In these communal roosts there is often a considerable outburst
of social singing. In London in the last century these places where
house sparrows gathered and sang before going to roost were known
as "chapels". There is some doubt whether these are actual
roosting places or merely pre-roosting collecting points.

The behaviour in the morning is usually much less conspicuous,
though the air of excitement is still present. On some mornings
there may be a little social singing but this is not prolonged and the
roost is usually cleared half an hour after the first birds have
wakened up.

The house sparrow has a remarkably short working day compared with most passerine species. The birds are normally in the
roost before sunset and do not get up much before sunrise; this may

PLATE 11. Tree nest: *above*, winter; *below*, spring. These open nests require considerable maintenance after the winter storms. (*C. W. Teager*)

PLATE 12. Although a social breeder, house-sparrow nests in a tree are
usually well separated. (*C. W. Teager*)

be contrasted with robins and blackbirds that are active until darkness is almost complete and can be heard on the move again before they can be seen the following morning. Perhaps this liking for his bed is picked up by the sparrow from his close association with man! In the short winter days some birds spend over sixteen hours roosting each day and even at the summer solstice as much as nine hours may be spent sleeping. In the Arctic at 68°N in continuous daylight it has been reported that house sparrows roosted for four hours, longer than other passerines at this latitude. In urban areas sparrows frequently share the same hole with starlings; when this is the case roosting is rather delayed as the sparrows are unable to enter before the larger species has settled down.

Although there is not the same activity among individuals or pairs that roost in their nest one gets the same impression of excitement. The birds are very restless and do not slip unobtrusively into their nests. When both members of the pair roost in the nest together the cock usually waits until his hen is in before going in himself and is invariably first up in the morning. It is interesting that, where the hen only of the pair roosts in the nest, the cock almost invariably joins her at the entrance to the nest and stays until she is safely in bed before going off to his own hole or joining the communal roost; even in the morning he frequently arrives before the hen is up and calls her from the nest.

Activities like dust-bathing and water-bathing, to which the sparrow is much addicted, are, as I have already described in an earlier chapter, frequently performed by numbers of birds together. The infectious nature of almost any form of behaviour is very noticeable; for example, as soon as one individual begins to bathe it is imitated by several others and the same can be said of things like nest building and sexual behaviour. Communal activity ensures that the behaviour is adopted when conditions are suitable and also provides a measure of safety in that the birds taking part are less likely to be surprised by a predator.

CHAPTER II

MOVEMENTS, MIGRATION
AND SEDENTARY BEHAVIOUR

IN TEMPERATE and sub-arctic regions there is a seasonal fluctuation in the availability of food. The majority of types of both vegetable and animal foods are most plentiful in the summer months and scarcest in the winter. If this food supply is to be exploited at its time of abundance, some provision has to be made for the period of scarcity. Animals living in these regions have solved this problem in a number of ways: some do without the need for food during the period of seasonal shortage by hibernating or changing to a chrysalis form, others migrate to a different region where food is available. Birds, if we except the somewhat doubtful case of the American whip-poor-will, do not hibernate and either avoid the period of food scarcity by migration or stick it out if conditions are not too severe. Both these solutions involve considerable hazards: migration imposes a severe physical strain and if adverse weather conditions occur during the migration period large numbers may get drifted off course and perish out at sea; sedentary species, while avoiding the dangers of migration, run the risk of winter food shortage. We should expect the mortality of sedentary species to be high during the winter months, especially when weather conditions are more severe than normal. Indeed after severe winters in this country marked decreases in the population of resident birds have been noted.

Certain birds, on the other hand, seem to get the best of both worlds. These are species that have become closely associated with man and by living close to him during the winter months seldom suffer food shortage, of such birds the house sparrow is the outstanding example. In the different habitats occupied by sparrows there is generally no winter food shortage: birds living on farms manage to subsist on grain and food put out for chickens and pigs; those in suburbia are generally well provided for by food put out on bird tables; while those living in factories can usually pick up scraps from luncheon packets if food is not deliberately provided for them. Where food is put out regularly in hen runs or for birds in gardens, sparrows soon learn the time that it appears and to associate any calls or sounds connected with its appearance, so that they obtain the maximum benefit. That house sparrows in Britain do not normally suffer from starvation in the winter is shown by the mortality data in Chapter 13 and also by observation of the birds themselves, which shows that they have to spend only a comparatively small proportion of even the winter day in searching for food; at times when winters have been exceptionally severe some reduction in numbers has been reported, though the house sparrow does not suffer to anything like the same extent as other small resident birds.

The extremely sedentary nature of the house sparrow is shown by following the life of birds marked with colour-rings; as I have already said, once these birds have adopted a nest site, they spend most of their lives within a few hundred yards of it, except when they join the grain-field flocks at the end of the summer. Even this movement is limited: few adults move as far as two miles from their nest at this time of the year. At any other season very few days pass without the birds being seen at their nests, though in a few exposed places in Britain sparrows are said to move out in the winter months.

Recoveries of house sparrows ringed in Great Britain, Continental Europe and North America confirm the impression given by watching colour-ringed birds. Table 13 gives details of recoveries of house sparrows ringed in Great Britain and in western Europe. The British results are obtained from the British Trust for Ornithology ringing recoveries; those from western Europe are taken from two sources: first a summary of ringing recoveries collected by B. Rademacher, secondly results from one very large local effort by F. Preiser near Stuttgart already referred to in Chapter 2.

These latter results have been separated because they are not strictly comparable with the others. In this large experiment 5,143 house sparrows were ringed in the three years 1952–4 in the months May to October and each succeeding winter large scale poisoning

TABLE 13

Movements by Ringed House Sparrows

Region	No. of recoveries at distances:			Total birds
	up to 2 km. (1¼ miles)	2–10 km.	over 10 km. (6 miles)	
British Isles	840 (92·3%)	48 (5·3%)	22 (2·4%)	910
W. Europe	224 (89·2%)	16 (6·4%)	11 (4·4%)	251
S. Germany	785 (90·1%)	82 (9·1%)	7 (0·8%)	874

actions against house sparrows were carried out in the same area. As we have seen, much of the movement or dispersal of sparrows takes place in the period up to their first breeding—if Rademacher's results are separated into adults and juveniles, the proportion in the over ten kilometre group are 3·2 per cent and 6·7 per cent respectively, showing a greater tendency to movement in the young birds—hence it is probable that the poisonings would interfere with this dispersal and these results would exhibit a smaller degree of movement than takes place in more normal circumstances. In other words the proportion of the birds in the 2–10 kilometre group is inflated with birds that might have moved further afield in the spring if they had not been killed off in the winter; Preiser's important results, which throw much light on house sparrow dispersal, must therefore be considered separately.

The most striking feature of the ringing results is the remarkably sedentary behaviour of the bird. This is underlined when it is appreciated that the majority of house sparrows ringed are juveniles that have not yet settled down to breed, the very birds that are most prone to movement. The other point of interest from the table is the slightly greater tendency for movement in the Continental birds; this is true, of course, of many other species that are resident in the British Isles and partial migrants on the Continent.

Examination of the few recoveries in the highest range group, further details of which are given in Appendix IV, suggests a definite southerly movement for immature birds ringed in the summer and a less clearly defined northerly trend for birds ringed in the winter and recovered during the breeding season (Fig. 19, below). Considerably more recovery data are required before this suggestion can be confirmed. A regular migration is, however, undertaken by some Italian sparrows (*P. d. italiae*)—a clearly marked sub-species of the house sparrow; this bird is confined to Italy in the breeding season but small numbers regularly winter in southern France. Two individuals ringed at La Tour du Valat in the Camargue in the winter of 1953 were subsequently recovered in Piedmont in Italy. There is also evidence of migration of the sub-species *domesticus* into northern Italy where they can be readily distinguished from the local birds (*italiae*) in the autumn and winter.

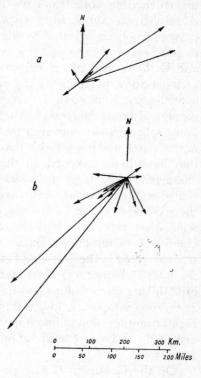

There is considerable visual evidence of house sparrow movement on the east coast of England from Yorkshire to Kent. Flocks of birds have been reported from September to November either moving southwards with other migrants or turning up at places where they are not usually to be seen. T. H. Nelson writing on the birds of Yorkshire in 1907 quoted several cases of "rushes" of house

FIG. 19. Seasonal differences in house sparrow movements based on recoveries of birds ringed in Great Britain and Western Europe.

a. Birds ringed in winter and recovered in summer.
b. Birds ringed in summer and recovered in winter.

sparrows at Spurn in October and November, and C. B. Ticehurst has given instances of movement on the Suffolk coast in both spring and autumn. However, no recent evidence of similar movements has come from the Bird Observatory that has been established at Spurn since 1945. On the other hand, autumn passage has been reported by the Observatory at Gibraltar Point in Lincolnshire in the past few years in September and October, and D. Lack in a recent migration watch in the second half of October 1952, in which a number of watchers distributed mainly over the east Kent coast took part, reported a definite southward passage of house sparrows at the South Foreland. Movements of house sparrows were not seen by the other observers co-operating in this watch and it is possible that these movements and the others that have been recorded on the east coast are purely local in character. Very large numbers of house sparrows have been ringed on the east coast, particularly at the Bird Observatories, and the recoveries so far do not suggest a regular movement on any scale. Very recently a bird ringed in England has crossed to the Continent—a full-grown female ringed at Portland in July 1959 was recovered in the following February in Cherbourg. As we shall see later (Chapter 15) there are numerous reports of sparrows hitch-hiking aboard ships and this possibility cannot be ruled out in the present case. I do not think the suggestion that there is a regular immigration of house sparrows from the Continent can be accepted without considerably more evidence from ringing recoveries.

On the Continent of Europe visible evidence of migration is rather similar to that in Great Britain, though the records from the south of Sweden suggesting movement across the southern Baltic are rather more numerous. Again, comparison with other species suggests that the proportion of birds taking part in any movement must be small. H. Gatke writing at the end of the last century considered that most of the breeding house sparrows on Heligoland left the island in the winter and were replaced by a different wintering population. Since Gatke's time four birds ringed on Heligoland have been recovered in Schleswig-Holstein giving support to his ideas: one of these was a bird born on the island, the others were ringed as first-year birds in the winter; thus both could be further evidence of a dispersal of immature birds rather than of true migration.

Further information on the nature of the movement that does take place is given by the appearance of house sparrows on coastal islands where they do not breed. The seasonal distribution on islands round Britain (Isle of May, Farnes, Havergate, Lundy, Skokholm, Skomer and St. Kilda) is given in Table 14.

TABLE 14

Appearance of House Sparrows at British Coastal Islands

	Mar	Apr	May	Jun	Jul	Aug	Sep	Oct	Nov
No. of Records	1	4	6	2	0	1	0	0	2

All of these records refer to single individuals with the exception of a flock of eight on the Farnes in November 1882; they are thus more suggestive of a wandering rather than a true migration. A most unexpected appearance was that of a bird at the observatory on Ben Nevis (4,406 ft.) on 12th September, 1895. C. Kruger, who has reviewed the records of house sparrows killed at lighthouses in the Kattegat and round the Danish coast in the period 1883–1944, found rather a similar pattern to that for Britain given in Table 14 except perhaps that the autumn occurrences were a little more frequent. The picture is again one of dispersal rather than of true directed migration.

From the information available the house sparrow appears to be just as sedentary in other parts of its range as it is in Europe, with the exception of the races living in the area between the Caspian and the Himalayas. The birds breeding in Turkestan and northern Afghanistan (*P.d. bactrianus*) and those of southern Afghanistan, northern Pakistan (Baluchistan and N.W. Frontier), Kashmir, southern Tibet and Nepal (*P.d. parkini*) are almost entirely summer visitors, migrating southwards to the plains of Pakistan (Sind) and India in the winter months. In Ladak, for example, the birds are only present from May until August, although at lower altitudes in Kashmir occasional wintering birds are found. In Turkestan the birds also stay only a short time in the summer and rear only one brood. Of all the races of house sparrows these two are least closely associated with man. Some breed in holes in the roofs of houses but many breed away from man in colonies in cliffs and in holes in walls and earth banks. In the winter, when their range overlaps with that of the sedentary Indian race (*P.d. indicus*), the northern birds are to be found in flocks away from man's habitations, while the local birds remain near their breeding areas as they do in Europe.

Results of transplanting experiments, which are summarised in Table 15, confirm the expectation that the homing instinct would not be highly developed in the house sparrow. I should expect that young birds that have not bred and become attached to a particular nest site would probably settle down where they were released. The homing instinct would probably be stronger in an adult that had bred; however, as it is not certain which of the above records refer to such birds, we do not know from what distance they would be able to return.

TABLE 15
Results of House Sparrow Transplanting Experiments

Place birds caught	No.	Date	Place of Release	Remarks
Isle of May, Scotland	14		Anstruther, Fife, 6 m. WNW	None returned
Sway, Hampshire	1	1.5.32	3 m. away	Found dead Sway 12.5.32
Wilmslow, Cheshire	1	25.6.36	2½ m. away	Recovered dead where released, 8.8.36
Virginia Water, Berks	1♂	30.4.49	Sunninghill, 2 m. W.	Found dead Virginia Water, 30.7.51
Richmond, Surrey	9		S. Kensington, 8 m. NE.	Released singly, 4 returned
Richmond, Surrey	7		do.	Released as flock, none returned
Richmond, Surrey	5		do.	do.

Place birds caught	No.	Date	Place of Release	Remarks
Hermitage, Berks.	1♂	20.4.57	7 m. N.	Returned and bred
Jersey	10	Winter 1950–1	1½ m. away	7 returned
Jersey	12	,,	2¾ m. away	2 returned
Jersey	?	,,	5 m. away	1 returned
Drewitz, Germany	29	Oct. 1933	Potsdam, 4 m. away	2 recovered Drewitz; 1 on 29.10.33 other on 12.5.34
Essen, Germany	19	April 1960	Mulheim 10 m. WSW	Returned on two separate occasions
Sempach, Switzerland			Lucerne 10 m. away	Birds settled where released, although some had partly built nests
Henri-Chapelle, Belgium	1	Dec. 1932	Seraing, 13 m. WSW released May 1933	Recovered 1½ m. from where trapped, 11.6.33
Cracow, Poland	1♀	16.6.39	Zabierzów, 8 m. W.	Did not return
Cornell University, U.S.A.		Winter 1936–7	Distances up to 100 m.	Some returned from 5, 10, 20 and 30 m. but none from greater distances

As we have already seen, considerable flocks of house sparrows are formed in the late summer and autumn at grain fields. These large flocks are drawn from colonies nesting within a mile or two and when the flocks break up it appears that the young birds get scattered over the area from which the flock was drawn. In the Hampshire study area trapping and ringing of the birds was carried out in the area of Colony 1 (see Chapter 10 and Fig. 17, p. 103). The grain field flock was formed at E and consisted of birds from Colonies 1 to 5 inclusive. As a result of the dispersal of the young birds ringed in Colony 1, a small proportion of ringed birds was gradually built up in each of the other four colonies. It is interesting that ringed birds were not found in Colonies 23, 24 and 25, which did not appear to join the flock at E but rather formed a separate feeding flock in some grain fields lying to the south.

Observations on young birds colour-ringed before they joined the flock and others that were caught after the flock had dispersed showed that these birds moved freely between the neighbouring colonies during the autumn and winter months and did not settle down in a particular breeding colony until they had acquired a mate and a nest. As we have seen, once this occurred the birds remained faithful to their colony area for life.

Some of the young birds bred on Hilbre Island that left in the autumn returned after an absence of a month or two or, even more surprising, in their second year after being away for their first summer. These birds stayed only for a week or so but their appearance suggests that even the birds that disperse retain some memory of the colony of their birth.

In the Stockton area the grain-field flock was much larger, about five thousand birds compared to five hundred in the Hampshire area, and drew birds from a rather larger area, the birds I was marking travelling about three-quarters of a mile. This in turn led to a rather greater dispersal as can be seen by the recoveries of ringed birds shown in Fig. 20. These include both adults trapped when foraging in the study colony area away from their own breeding area and young birds that have dispersed in a similar way to those in the rural study area.

Preiser's investigation already mentioned has provided most useful information on the local movements of house sparrows. Figure 21, which is taken from his paper, shows the area in which his investigations were carried out. It is divided into four zones: in Zone 1 no ringing was carried out and the sparrow population was reduced each winter from 1951 to 1956 by extensive poisoning; 5,143 sparrows were ringed in Zone 2 from May to October in the years 1952 to 1954—no poisoning was carried out in this zone; no ringing was carried out in Zone 3 and winter poisoning campaigns

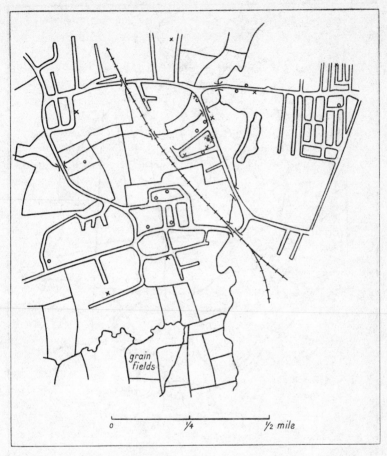

FIG. 20. Recoveries of ringed house sparrows in the suburban study area.
● ringing station.
x young birds ringed Aug-Nov.
o adults ringed May-Aug.

were carried out in 1953–4 and 1954–5; in Zone 4 there was neither ringing nor poisoning. As a result of the poisonings in Zone 1 the sparrow population was reduced by about sixty per cent. In this way a sparrow-poor area (Zone 1) was created on one side of the

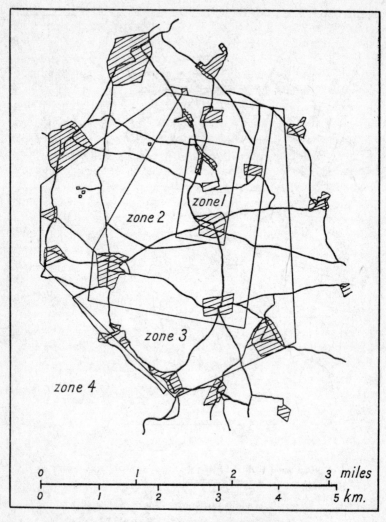

FIG. 21. Map of area near Stuttgart. (Studied by F. Preiser.)
The marked zones have the following significance:
Zone 1 – population reduced by poisoning in winters 1951-56
Zone 2 – Sparrows ringed 1952-54
Zone 3 – population reduced by poisoning in winters 1953-55
Zone 4 – no interference with sparrows

ringing zone while on the other side the population was at its normal level in the winter of 1953–4 and possibly slightly reduced in the following winter. In the winter of 1953–4 835 sparrows were poisoned in Zone 1 and 543 in Zone 3; of the former twenty-one (2·5 per cent) were ringed, whereas only two (0·3 per cent) of the latter were ringed. In the following winter the results were as follows: Zone 1, 436 poisoned, of which twelve (2·7 per cent) were ringed; Zone 3, 764 poisoned, of which four (0·5 per cent) were ringed. This very clearly indicates that there was significantly more immigration into the area where the population was below its normal level than into the area where the population was normal. The majority of the birds ringed by Preiser were juveniles and hence these results predominantly refer to the dispersal of first-year birds.

Colonial behaviour, if maintained throughout the year could lead to complete isolation and inbreeding that could be harmful in small populations. This does not normally occur in the house sparrow because of the formation of the grain-field flocks and the consequent dispersion of the young birds over the area from which the flock has been drawn. We can distinguish three classes of movement which are broadly covered by the range limits given in Table 13. First we have the normal foraging movements by adult birds. This is usually confined to one to two miles from the nest-site, the upper limit being only reached in the movement to the grain field in the summer. Secondly we have the dispersal of the young birds over the area from which the grain-field flock is drawn—an upper limit for this appears to be about six miles. Finally we have true migration which occurs regularly in some sub-species of the house sparrow and remains as a relict among some European birds. Preiser's results suggest that the young birds disperse and settle down in areas where the population is below the normal level for that area. The way in which young birds recognise when the population is below normal is obscure but so also are the factors actually controlling the population; possibly autumn nest-site prospecting may be of value in indicating which colonies are below their potential levels.

House sparrows appear to be very reluctant to move even

short distances across country that is unsuitable for them. Hence in winter and early spring they are largely confined to the breeding areas and their surroundings, but with the ripening of weed seeds and grain the area of suitable ground extends and habitats that are isolated in the winter become contiguous at other times of the year. This extreme sedentary behaviour and reluctance to move across, to them, unsuitable country no doubt explains the rather patchy distribution of the house sparrow in sub-optimum habitats, for example in Persia and parts of India.

Much of the dispersal in the autumn is merely local, but there is some evidence for rather more extensive movement towards the south-west. These birds probably settle down where they are and do not make a reverse migration in the spring. On the other hand, a second dispersal takes place at the beginning of the breeding season among those birds that are unable to find suitable nest-sites in established breeding colonies. This is shown by the ringing recoveries in Fig. 19, p. 117, and by the records for appearances at coastal islands, which reach a maximum in May (Table 14). The ringing recoveries suggest that the main direction of movement at this time of year for European birds is to the north-east.

However we look at it, the amount of dispersal is small. One consequence of this is that it could easily result in the formation of genetically isolated populations in which local strains, differing slightly from each other, could develop. As a result of large scale poisoning campaigns that have been carried out in Germany since the war it has been possible to obtain sufficient material from different populations to test whether this has occurred. Comparison of the wing lengths of birds from thirteen localities in Germany (eight in North Rhine-Westphalia; three in Saxony-Anhalt and two in Württemberg-Baden) and one in England (measurements on trapped birds at Stockton-on-Tees) showed that significant differences in the size of both males and females existed between over half of the pairs of populations and furthermore the sizes of the males and females in the same population were positively correlated, suggesting that the differences between populations had a genetical basis. When the sizes are averaged over large areas, as distinct from these local populations, it is apparent that there is a gradual increase in size from west to east across Europe. The local populations show random fluctuations about the mean for the particular longitude and in fact the Stockton-on-Tees birds were distinctly larger than the birds of some of the German local populations.

Resident species, provided they can obtain sufficient food during the period of scarcity, have the advantage over migratory ones that the hazards of migration are avoided. Extreme sedentary behaviour has the further advantage that the bird becomes very familiar with the area in which it lives; good feeding areas are well known and probably also the ways of cats and other local hazards of the district. Nesting sites are maintained throughout the year and little energy is wasted in disputes over them; breeding can begin as soon as conditions are favourable and, as no storage of energy reserves before migration is necessary, the birds have an extended breeding season enabling them to rear three or even four broods in succession.

CHAPTER 12

DISEASE AND PARASITES

VERY LITTLE is known about the causes of death in wild birds. Predation, disease, accidents and the hazards of migration each take their toll, though the significance of the different factors is not known for any particular species; indeed it may vary from season to season and year to year. The main reason for this lack of knowledge is that only a very small proportion of the birds that die each year are found and very few of these find their way to anyone sufficiently qualified to carry out a post-mortem examination. In recent years Dr. A. R. Jennings at Cambridge has asked for freshly dead birds to be sent to him. The sample obtained in this way is almost certainly a biased one; particularly with small birds it is most probable that the ones found have died from a violent accident or by poisoning—birds weakened by disease or starvation are likely to be taken by predators and disappear without trace. Nevertheless, this investigation has already given some fascinating information.

Jennings has reported on the death of fifty house sparrows: twenty-four of these were caused by trauma; nineteen by poisoning and the remaining seven by disease, including coccidiosis, aspergillosis, pneumonia and enteritis. The pathogenic organisms responsible for disease are grouped into four classes: viruses, bacteria, fungi and protozoa, all of which have been reported from house sparrows in various parts of the world. The virus infections include colds and canary pox, the bacterial ones anthrax (*Bacillus anthracis*), avian tuberculosis (*Mycobacterium*), pullorum disease (*Salmonella pullorum*) relapsing fever (*Treponema anserinum*) and equine encephalitis. Two fungal parasites that have been recorded are *Aspergillus fumigatus*, a common mould of the soil that causes a disease of the lungs and air-sacs (aspergillosis), and a sarcosporidium causing a disease of the muscles known as avian sarcosporidiosis. It is not known how widespread any of the diseases are among wild house sparrow populations. Coccidia, protozoan gut parasites, seem to be very common in sparrows; for example, they were present in forty-three out of fifty-four birds examined at Princeton in the U.S.A. All of these were healthy birds and it is not known why the balance is sometimes upset in favour of the protozoa and coccidiosis results. This gives rise to internal bleeding and may cause the death of the host. Another group of protozoans, which causes a disease of the white blood corpuscles, has been recorded from India, Italy, Great Britain and the United States. R. Lainson has recently investigated the life history of this parasite in British sparrows and has named the species *Lankesterella* (*Atoxoplasma*) *garnhami;* he found it to be present in all of ninety-nine adult and one hundred and fifty juveniles collected in Hertfordshire. This is an important patho-genic organism—Lainson observed that it caused the death of a number of young birds.

Epidemics causing very large mortalities of house sparrows are known, though the organisms responsible have not been identified. J. M. Stenhouse reported an epidemic in Fair Isle in 1926 that reduced the numbers from an estimated eight hundred birds to about forty in September and to less than ten by the winter. Similar decreases were found at the same time in Shetland—the bird became extinct on Mid Yell in 1928, though sparrows in the north and south of the island were unaffected—where it was reported that the birds' heads swelled so that their eyes were almost bursting before they died and by 1928 the disease appears to have spread to Perthshire, though it was becoming attenuated. A further outbreak of a similar kind has been reported from Mid Yell in 1957. The effect of environmental factors at the extremity of the bird's range in Shetland may have rendered the birds there less resistant to disease. A marked decrease in the numbers of house sparrows was noticed in parts of the south of France during the first world war; an enquiry into the circumstances was made but unfortunately did not reach any definite conclusions. At least one observer thought that an epidemic was responsible; in St. Gèniès de Malgoires, Dépt. Gard, numerous dead birds were seen lying around in the winter of 1915–6 and it was reported that even the housewives remarked that the sparrows no longer came to steal the

HS-K

grain thrown out for the poultry. Striking decreases were noted in Arriège in 1916, Ain in 1917, Aude in 1918 and Côte d'Or in 1919, but whether these could be attributed to an epidemic is not known; in the last-mentioned Départment at least, the numbers recovered to their previous level within twenty months. Unfortunately in none of the cases was any pathological examination of specimens carried out so that the cause of death was not ascertained.

As well as these microparasites, house sparrows, in common with other animals, have their quota of internal macroparasites. These include worms—trematodes: *Collyriculum faba*, the sparrow fluke and *Prosthogonimus ovatus*, the oviduct fluke; nematodes: *Capillaria exile*, *Cheilospirura skrjabini* and *Microtetrameres inernis*—and mites: *Megostigmata,* inhabiting the lungs, e.g. *Ptylonyssus nudus*, which I have obtained from birds in Co. Durham. Again it is not known how far these are responsible for death; heavy infestations that could prove fatal usually only occur in young or diseased birds, though many individuals harbour some—thirty-one per cent of sixty-four young sparrows examined at Madison, Wisconsin, in 1910 were found to be infested with trematodes.

External parasites are much less likely to cause death than internal ones, though heavy infestations of blood-sucking types may be responsible for the mortality of nestlings and of course may be vectors for virus disease. Many of the ectoparasites are feeders on feathers and the horny layers of the skin and cause no great harm to their hosts, though severe infestations during the moult may interfere with the proper growth of the new feathers. I have found a number of hen house sparrows that had very poorly formed feathers on the underparts giving them a characteristic bluish-grey coloration. This is probably caused by feather feeding parasites during the growth of the feathers and it persists until the following moult is completed. For some reason the condition does not occur, or is certainly not as common, in males.

During the four years 1954–8 I collected ectoparasites from over four hundred and fifty live house sparrows at Stockton-on-Tees using the chloroform vapour technique. This method does not give truly quantitative results as some birds flap more than others and thus dislodge the anaesthetised parasites more completely; further the head of the bird has to be kept out of the vapour so that head-living species tend to be missed. Nevertheless it is possible to get some idea in this way of the types represented and their seasonal frequency. Feather mites were obtained from over half of the birds examined and there are probably few sparrows completely free of them; the number varied greatly from bird to bird, up to two hundred being collected from some individuals. Lice and fleas were found on about seven per cent of the birds and usually only a few were obtained from each bird; large numbers are only found on unhealthy birds or those with damaged mandibles. This technique appears to be an effective way of collecting fleas and the figure of seven per cent is probably quantitatively correct for the particular population of birds examined. Louse-flies were only obtained from two birds.

The greatest number of mites obtained were *Proctophyllodes* sp. (probably *P. passerina*, which has been recorded from the house sparrow, but specific identification is difficult as a number of species have been described by different workers and it is likely that some of these are synonymous—there appeared to be two male forms in the mites collected in Stockton) with odd individuals of *Dermoglyphus elongatus*, a species living inside the quills, *Glycophagus* sp., a free-living mite that feeds on organic matter, and *Dermanyssus gallinae*, the poultry red mite, a blood-sucking species that lives in the nest rather than on the bird. One nest in America was estimated to contain eighteen thousand mites of this last species; it is probably collected in the chicken feathers used in lining the nest. The house sparrow is also a host for the related *D. avium*, which is found on cage birds in America and *Microlichus avium* a feather mite living next to the skin. A number of ticks have been found on house sparrows, including *Argas reflexus* (the pigeon tick), *Ixodes passericola* and a variety of other casual visitors, such as *Haemaphysalis leporispalustris* (the snow-shoe hare tick) in the U.S.A. According to M. Rothschild and T. Clay ticks are very dangerous to their hosts; they may act as vectors for disease (e.g. relapsing fever) and also their saliva, which they inject into the host, may be toxic. Lainson considers that the mite *Dermanyssus Gallinae* is responsible for the transmission of the protozoan *Lankesterella,* which as already mentioned can cause the death of young birds.

The Mallophaga collected from the Stockton birds included almost equal numbers of *Menacanthus annulatus,* a member of the superfamily Amblycera, which feed on blood in addition to feathers, *Brüelia cyclothorax* (=*subtilis*) and *Philopterus fringillae;* the last two are members of the superfamily Ischnocera and feed only on feathers, the latter being confined to the head. *Degeeriella vulgata,* also of this superfamily, has been recorded from house sparrows in the U.S.A. W. J. Woodman and R. J. Dicke, who examined 391 house sparrows in Wisconsin immediately after death, found fifty-five per cent of the birds to be infested by Mallophaga (mainly *Brüelia* sp. with much smaller numbers of *Menacanthus* sp.). *Myrsidea quadrifasciata* and *Cuclotogaster heterographus* have also been reported.

Thirty-five fleas were collected, the most on one bird being three; these included almost equal numbers of *Ceratophyllus gallinae* and *C. fringillae. Gallinae* is found more frequently in house sparrow nests than any other flea; at times the population of one nest may be quite considerable, for example seventy-nine were found in a nest at Pittodrie, Aberdeen, on 24th May. Because of the presence of this flea house sparrow nests are frequently inhabited by the beetle *Gnathoncus punctulatus,* which preys on it. This flea was introduced to America with house sparrows and has now spread there on to poultry and numerous wild birds. Other fleas have been recorded from house sparrows but appear to be only casual for this host. *Ornithomyia fringillina* seems to be the only hippoboscid found on house sparrows; only two were obtained from the Stockton birds, though H. N. Southern found many young sparrows on the Isle of May in 1937 to be infested with this fly, up to ten occurring on one bird. The larvae of some dipterous flies live in the nests of birds and suck the blood of the nestlings. The larvae of both the bird bottle fly (*Protocalliphera azurea*) and the nest fly (*Neottiophilum praeustum*) have been recorded from house sparrow nests, though the species does not appear to be a common host. Further information on the insect ectoparasites of the house sparrow is given in a review by G. B. Thompson. In addition to fleas and the parasitic flies,

PLATE 13. Male feeding young in tree nest; insect food is mainly brought when the nestlings are only a few days old. (*W. E. Higham*)

PLATE 14. Female feeding young: when the young are within a few days of fledging they come to the nest entrance to be fed. (*J. Markham*)

house sparrows' nests, which as we have seen may be used for breeding and roosting continuously for a number of years, support a varied fauna of scavenging insects, including beetles, moth larvae and mites; these are of little significance to the sparrow but the harbourage provided to the larvae of clothes moths and carpet beetles in nests close to houses may be undesirable from man's point of view.

The main enemies of the house sparrow are: birds of prey, in particular owls (barn, long-eared and tawny), sparrow-hawks and kestrels; cats and, in certain circumstances, man himself. There are a number of records of rings that had been put on sparrows being subsequently found in owls' pellets. The owls take the sparrows by beating them out of communal roosts in bushes at night and also inside buildings as has already been described. Long-eared owls particularly seem to prey on sparrows, which have been found to be the commonest of the bird preys taken by this species: in studies made in Britain, Germany, Holland and Iraq, house sparrows made up from twenty-five to seventy-five per cent of the birds eaten, birds forming about twenty per cent of the food of this owl. A recent study of the food taken by town-living tawny owls showed that birds made up most of their diet, with the house sparrow the principle prey taken. Sparrow-hawks are of less significance, as far as sparrows are concerned, in this country than they are on the Continent since they are so much less numerous. In a study in Holland, for example, L. Tinbergen estimated that sparrow-hawks accounted for a little over eight per cent of the house sparrow population in the area studied in May—921 carcases were found at one nest—and that this represented about eighty per cent of the house sparrows dying in that month; O. Uttendörfer, in a study of the food brought to nestling sparrow-hawks in Germany, found that house sparrows were the most numerous bird prey species. Sparrow-hawks may also have a considerable effect on large aggregations of sparrows at roosts, as we have seen in Chapter 10. Although rings placed on house sparrows have been found in their nests, kestrels appear to be less serious predators; I have watched a kestrel and house sparrows feeding together at the same corn stack, the former on mice and the latter

on the grain and although the sparrows were nervous of the
kestrel they remained in the area and continued to feed. The habit
of taking sparrows appears to be largely confined to town-living
kestrels. The domestic cat is an important predator of the house
sparrow and is responsible for many rings being recovered from
corpses brought into houses; E. R. Kalmbach reports that a
stomach analysis of a feral cat obtained in Pennsylvania showed
that the house sparrow accounted for a tenth of the food. Both
adult and young birds are taken. Other predators that have been
recorded are: dog, mallard, moorhen, heron, black-headed gull,
peregrine, shrikes and eel. These are more of academic interest,
however, than of biological importance, though a case recently
reported to me of a crow that specialised on sparrows is probably
of more significance. This bird would perch close to a house and as
soon as a sparrow had disappeared into a crevice would fly there
and take the unfortunate bird as it came out. It is not known if this
behaviour was confined to one individual, but, after it had been
observed, there appeared to be a reduction of the sparrow population in the neighbourhood.

The main cause of accidental death is the motor car, which
takes a particularly heavy toll of young birds. I have found considerable numbers of dead birds on roads under trees where they have
been collecting insects that have fallen from the foliage and both
R. G. Finnis and N. L. Hodson in separate studies of road
casualties in England found that the house sparrow was by far the
most frequently affected species, with a marked peak during the
period of summer and early autumn flocking when large numbers
of inexperienced young birds were killed. Accidental poisoning
from bait put out for vermin is another not uncommon cause of
death. Cases of drowning, particularly of birds caught by a severe
thunderstorm in an open roost, and of birds flying into windows are
less common, but the bird that died under a fall of snow from a roof
and the other at Lord's by a delivery from a fast bowler were rather
unlucky.

It can be seen from this brief survey how little, in fact, is really
known about the hazards of this bird's life. Quite minor ailments
among animals, where competition for existence is high, may be

enough to result in death, either by predation or by the bird's inability to find food; this latter factor may be particularly important in small birds that are unable to stand long fasting. S. C. Kendeigh in America has shown that house sparrows deprived of food were unable to survive for long; about freezing point the limit was only fifteen hours, though at higher temperatures this was somewhat extended, the difference depending on the amount of energy required to maintain the body temperature. During periods of extreme cold, the birds' behaviour is directed at conservation of energy; the time is divided between spells of intense feeding activity and resting in sheltered places with the feathers fluffed out to give the minimum heat loss. In a recent study of the feeding problems of the house sparrow in winter in Minnesota, J. R. Beer found that during spells of cold weather (average daily temperature less than $-20°C$) the birds began to feed before sunrise and feeding continued till after sunset. When the temperature was about zero, feeding began later and ended earlier; moreover the early morning feeding activity was noticeably less intense. This suggests that during the periods of low temperatures the birds may have been approaching the limit of their temperature tolerance. On the other hand birds seem to be able to live with quite major disabilities. A ringed cock at one of my nests lost his left leg on 16th March, 1957; despite this he successfully reared two broods that year and a further three in 1958. I have also seen birds blinded in one eye; none of these have been under close observation and it is not possible to say how long they survived, though a hen I trapped had a completely healed scar over one eye, suggesting that she had been blind for some time. Such birds have difficulty in landing on the branches of trees but otherwise do not seem to be at a great disadvantage; being a social species they may be able to escape from predators by heeding the warning cries of neighbours. There is a report of a blind fledgling being fed by an adult; however, as might be expected, it did not live for long after leaving the nest.

While the actual causes of death still remain obscure it is clear that in stable parts of the bird's range the excess in the population that is produced during the breeding season must die from

some cause or other before the beginning of the next breeding
season. Much more is known about the dynamics of house
sparrow populations and there is considerable information on
this subject from a variety of sources as we shall see in the following
chapter.

CHAPTER 13

EXPECTATION OF LIFE
AND MORTALITY

THERE ARE three phases in the life of higher animals: infancy, maturity and senility. The infantile period in the house sparrow lasts up to about the end of the year in which they are born; it is characterised by a high mortality rate, probably a result of inexperience and vulnerability to disease. Inexperience may lead to death both because of the greater risk of predation—C. Dixon, writing in 1909, remarked how in summer it was possible to watch rats preying on young sparrows feeding on crumbs, half-a-dozen being taken in a watch of thirty minutes—and possibly also through starvation, some individuals being unable to feed themselves when competition for food is severe; certainly many of these inexperienced young birds are killed by motor cars, a fate that much less frequently befalls the adults.

During the period of maturity the death rate is probably independent of age. It is not known how long this lasts; the longest lived individual according to recoveries of British ringed birds was about eight years old; a bird ringed in Bonn as a juvenile was found dead seven years and two months later, but the record for longevity goes to a wild sparrow ringed in August 1929 in Belgium and recovered dead eleven years three and a half months later. Several of my colour-ringed birds have bred for five successive seasons but, though two have lived into their sixth spring, neither bred, both dying soon after the start of the breeding season; it is interesting that Mrs. Kipps considered that, although her pet sparrow Clarence lived until he was twelve, his prime was reached when he was five or six years old. In the wild, few individuals, if any, survive until senility. Clarence had a stroke when he was eleven and certainly would not have survived but for the care and attention of his mistress; there is another record of a sparrow living in captivity in America for twelve years.

Much more precise information about survival rate and

expectation of life in nature can be obtained from ringing recoveries. These give exact details of the length of life after ringing and from this mortality can be worked out provided that wearing of the rings is not disadvantageous to the bird and also that rings are not lost before the death of the bird. The effect of these assumptions is not known. A few individuals, no doubt, die because their ring gets caught on a snag; this is probably not frequent and a bird I had under observation that lost a leg survived for two further breeding seasons with a ring on his remaining leg, suggesting this was no great handicap. There is a fair loss of plastic colour-rings, but loss of aluminium rings appears to be comparatively infrequent with the house sparrow; the birds do not seem able to remove the metal rings, as some individuals do with the plastic ones, and the most likely cause of loss is by the ring getting caught and unwrapping. Wear by abrasion and corrosion does not seem to be significant in the case of the sparrow.

The majority of house sparrow nests are relatively inaccessible and in consequence only a comparatively small number of nestlings can be ringed; hence it is not possible to calculate the mortality from the ringing results. However by considering the recoveries of fledglings ringed in May and June we can get some indication of the survival rate of birds about one month old, that is shortly after they have become independent of their parents. Ringing recoveries suggest that about twenty per cent of the birds born in these months survive until the next breeding season. Birds born in July and August have only about nine months to live until the breeding season and probably about twenty-five per cent of them live until then. (The annual survival rate of juveniles less than one month old is about twelve per cent.) Fig. 22 shows graphically month by month how a population of one hundred young birds decays. It will be seen that just over half survive their first month; thereafter the death rate steadily decreases each month and approaches that of the adults; for instance, for forty-eight birds ringed in December, which observations on colour-ringed individuals suggest are mainly in their first year, the survival rate was fifty-seven per cent, which as we shall see below is typical of the adult bird.

The annual adult survival rate based on the British Trust for

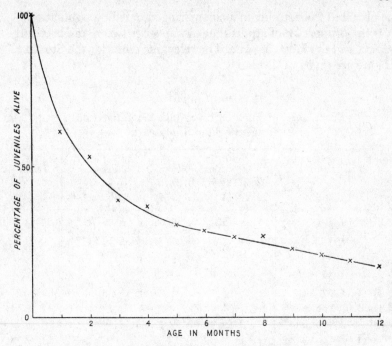

FIG. 22. Percentage mortality curve of juvenile house sparrows based on recoveries of nestlings and juveniles ringed in May and June. (Information from British Trust for Ornithology ringing recoveries.)

Ornithology ringing recoveries using J. B. S. Haldane's formula, which permits the use of recoveries of birds ringed in the last few years, some of which will die in the succeeding few years and provide further recovery results, is fifty-six per cent. The figure of fifty-six per cent is based on the recovery of almost four hundred house sparrows ringed as adults, neglecting those birds marked as hens or adults from May to September, when confusion may arise between hens and juveniles. More detailed examination of the results shows that there is no difference in survival rate between the sexes. A survival rate of fifty-six per cent means that fifty-six per cent of the birds alive at the beginning of one breeding season will survive until the next; hence the annual adult mortality can also be obtained from studies of a colour-ringed breeding population—it is the proportion of adults that disappear between one breeding season and the following one. The relevant results for the Stockton colony are given in Table 16.

TABLE 16

Survival Rate based on Lives of Colour-ringed Birds
in the Stockton Study Area

Year of Birth	Number alive on 1st April												Total	
	1954		1955		1956		1957		1958		1959			
	♂♂	♀♀	♂♂	♀♀	♂♂	♀♀	♂♂	♀♀	♂♂	♀♀	♂♂	♀♀		
1953	17	12	12	9	7	8	1	6	0	2	0	1		
1954	—	—	7	11	6	9	4	3	3	1	1	0		
1955	—	—	—	—	6	9	5	6	0	5	0	3		
1956	—	—	—	—	—	—	7	8	5	3	4	2		
1957	—	—	—	—	—	—	—	—	6	5	4	3		
													♂♂	♀♀
Total alive on 1st April of year	17	12	19	20	19	26	17	23	14	16	—	—	86	97
Total alive on 1st April of following year	12	9	13	17	10	15	8	11	9	9	—	—	52	61
Survival rate %	71	75	68	85	53	58	47	48	64	54	—	—	60	64
Survival rate both sexes combined	72		77		55		47		60		—		62	

The average survival rate estimated in this way over a period of five years is sixty-two per cent. This is in reasonable agreement with the figure of fifty-six per cent obtained from the ringing recoveries; the latter represents a mean for the whole country and it is quite possible that the survival rate differs from colony to colony and with different habitats. It is interesting to note that the survival rate fluctuates from year to year; the fact that the rates for both sexes fluctuate together suggests that this is a real effect and not just a random one caused by the small numbers involved. The

PLATE 15. The young are fed by their parents for about two weeks after they leave the nest.
(*C. W. Teager*)

PLATE 16. Young house sparrows: note the difference in head pattern; the two outside birds have white spots behind the eye, while the centre bird has a light stripe through the eye extending to the back of the head. (*C. W. Teager*)

results for my Hampshire colony were limited to two years and concerned only forty birds. The survival rate estimated from these was eighty-five per cent; this possibly indicates a higher survival rate for rural birds, though the observations are too few to be confident that this is the case. It would be most interesting to know whether the effect of being reared in an urban habitat, which probably means a smaller amount of insect food in the nestlings' diet, produces a slightly less viable strain of birds; this could reduce the resistance of the young to disease.

The ringing recoveries are of interest not only for the information they give about mortality but also because they show how mortality is distributed throughout the months of the year. It might be supposed with a sedentary species like the house sparrow that the greatest mortality would occur during the winter when weather is severe and the daylight hours, when food can be sought, are short; however, examination of the results shows the reverse to be the case, the maximum mortality occuring during the breeding season. It is interesting that E. M. Nicholson, who carried out counts of house sparrows in Kensington Gardens in the winter of 1925–6, found that the numbers barely changed during this period. The actual figures from the ringing recovery data are given in Table 17.

TABLE 17

Seasonal Distribution of Mortality from Ringing Recoveries

	Jan	Feb	Mar	Apr	May	Jun	Jul	Aug	Sep	Oct	Nov	Dec
♂♂ Number	11	11	28	39	37	46	32	17	7	10	11	14
%	6·5	4	10·5	14·5	13·5	17	12	6·5	2·5	3·5	4	5
♀♀ Number	14	8	12	28	38	45	32	9	7	13	17	8
%	6	3·5	5	12	16·5	19·5	14	4	3	5·5	7·5	3·5
Total adults Number	43	25	52	100	113	127	86	38	21	29	32	30
%	6	3·5	7·5	14·5	16·5	18·5	12·5	5·5	3	4	4·5	4·5

The "Total adults" in the Table is greater than the sum of the males and the females as it includes birds ringed when young and not sexed.

It should be mentioned that in a study of the sparrow population of Kiel, Frl. Fallet, on the other hand, found a higher winter loss, the population decreasing by about a third between the beginning of February and the beginning of April; there was no evidence to suggest an emigration of the birds and Frl. Fallet considered that the decrease was a result of shortage of food. A possible explanation of the difference between the two sets of results is that, whereas the British ringing recoveries give an average picture based on many years' results, the Kiel observations refer to only one season and may thus indicate an abnormal decrease resulting from some unusual circumstance, such as an exceptionally severe winter; on the other hand this could be a real feature of sparrow populations living in places where winter conditions are more severe than is normal in Britain as a whole.

It is possible now to indicate how a typical population of house sparrows may change throughout the year. This is done in Table 18, which is based on observations on adults in the suburban study area (the majority of which were colour-ringed) supplemented by breeding success data and the juvenile mortality curve given in Fig. 22, p. 139. To eliminate the random fluctuations that may occur from year to year and obtain a more general picture, the number of adults alive each month and the number of broods fledged have been summed over a five-year period. In this study area most of the nests were in the roofs of houses and were not accessible; thus while it was possible to determine the number of clutches raised by each pair and the date they fledged it was not possible to find out the fledging success for each brood. To obtain figures for the number of young fledged, the results from the British Trust for Ornithology Nest Record Cards (see Chapter 8) have been used. As the mortality of the juveniles is closely dependent on age, the fledgings for each month are treated separately, using the results of Fig. 22. In this way it is possible to estimate the number of juveniles in the population each month. The results in the Table are shown graphically in Fig. 23, p. 144, for a hypothetical population of one hundred adults at 1st April. It will be noticed that at the end of twelve months the population has returned to its original value; this, of course, would be expected in

TABLE 18

Seasonal composition of suburban population of house sparrows

	Apr	May	Jun	Jul	Aug	Sep	Oct	Nov	Dec	Jan	Feb	Mar	Apr
Adults alive on 1st of month	293	289	282	263	225	201	199	191	187	181	178	176	173
Broods fledged in previous month	—	1	42	70	57	32	2	—	—	—	—	—	—
Fledging success/brood	—	3·5	3·4	2·8	2·6	2·3	2·0	—	—	—	—	—	—
April fledgings	—	4	3	2	2	1	1	1	1	1	1	1	1
May fledgings	—	—	143	90	70	57	50	44	40	37	34	32	29
June fledgings	—	—	—	196	124	96	78	69	61	55	51	47	44
July fledgings	—	—	—	—	148	93	73	59	52	46	41	39	36
August fledgings	—	—	—	—	—	74	47	36	30	26	23	21	19
September fledgings	—	—	—	—	—	—	4	3	2	2	1	1	1
Total juveniles	—	4	146	288	344	321	253	212	186	167	151	141	130
Total adults and young	293	293	428	551	569	522	452	403	373	348	329	317	303

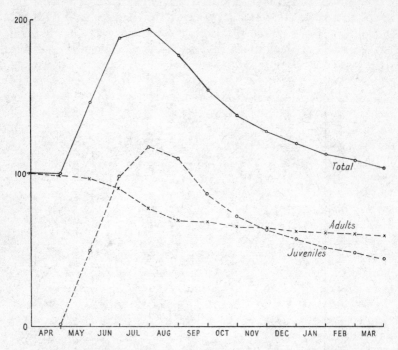

FIG. 23. Seasonal composition of suburban house sparrow population based on hypothetical population of 100 birds at start of breeding season.

a stable part of the bird's range, but it gives some justification for the assumptions made in constructing the Table. The results suggest that about twenty to twenty-five per cent of the young fledged can expect to survive to the next breeding season. As we have already seen from the ringing recoveries, the greatest mortality occurs during the breeding season. A **new** feature that emerges from the study is that, in spite of the high reproductive rate, the population at no stage reaches double its value at the start of the breeding season; the reason for this is the spread of breeding coupled with the extremely high mortality of the juveniles in their first few weeks of life.

The only other information available on the proportion of young in a population of house sparrows is given by M. Löhrl and R. Böhringer for 1,440 birds poisoned near Stuttgart, Germany, in December 1954. Dissection showed that sixty-seven per cent of these were first-year birds, whereas the proportion according to Table 18 at that time of the year is fifty per cent. This could indicate a real difference in mortality rate in a different part of the bird's range or it could be accounted for by the German sample being a slightly biased one, the young birds being less wary and accepting the poisoned bait more readily than the adults.

The house sparrow, while wary and distrustful of man, is not particularly difficult to trap; however, once handled the birds seldom allow themselves to be re-trapped. For instance, out of 820 birds I have trapped, only twenty-six (just over three per cent) have been taken a second time; R. W. Dexter in America re-trapped sixty-seven out of 668 birds (ten per cent)—all but two of these were juveniles. This is very different from other small garden birds like robins, dunnocks and tits, which regularly make use of known traps as feeding places.

The house sparrows I have ringed were mostly trapped in Potter traps (i.e. automatic traps catching one bird at a time) and the traps were set for approximately the same amount of time each month except for the limitation imposed by shorter daylight hours in the winter. The seasonal variation in trapping rate, which is shown in Fig. 24, p. 146, gives an interesting insight into the behaviour of the bird; the number of adults trapped shows a marked increase during the breeding season. At this period the adults become fully occupied with breeding duties and, having less time available to spend in seeking food, become less wary and take the risk of entering a trap that at other times of the year they would avoid. The number of juveniles shows a similar peak in the summer but by August and September few birds are being caught; this is because most of the birds have joined the grain-field flock and were not feeding in the breeding area where my traps were situated. In October there is another sharp rise but the numbers fall away rapidly reaching a minimum just before the start of the breeding season. The majority trapped over this period are the inexperienced first-year birds and the rate of trapping decreases as they become older and more wary. R. W. Dexter similarly reported that the number of sparrows caught in two funnel traps fell from several per day at the beginning of October to only one in ten days in December. This was not because of a reduction in the number of

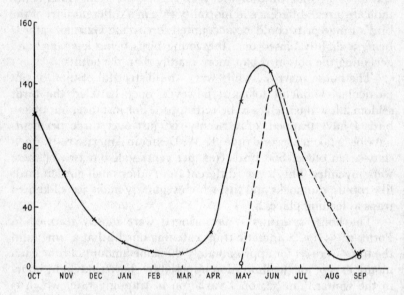

FIG. 24. Seasonal distribution of house sparrow trappings.
x Full grown   o Juveniles

birds but because they became more wary and also learned to find their way back out of the funnels.

The status of a proportion of the birds trapped is obtained by colour-ringing them and observing their behaviour. The views above are supported by consideration of the twenty-six individuals that were re-trapped: three of these were ringed as juveniles and re-trapped before the end of the same year; the remainder, apart from one caught the second time in October and another the second time in March, were caught during the breeding season while they were engaged either in incubating or feeding young.

The rather unexpected way in which the seasonal mortality rate varies is probably a result of the bird's connection with man. In most wild land animals living in temperate regions the seasonal food shortage presents a problem but, as already indicated in Chapter 11, the house sparrow avoids a scarcity of food in the winter by living close to man, who directly or indirectly provides ample food and, when winter conditions are particularly severe and natural food supplies become inaccessible, puts out extra food for birds. No other bird depends so completely on man; but those members of other species that inhabit gardens or have learned to take the "unnatural" foods provided by man might be expected to have a similar seasonal mortality. D. Snow has, in fact, shown this to be the case for a town population of blackbirds though it is not known if the country-living ones have the higher mortality in winter that would be expected.

Even in severe weather in winter when the days are short and, in temperate latitudes, only eight hours of daylight may be available for food seeking, observation shows that house sparrows appear to have little difficulty in finding sufficient food and in fact spend a considerable time in other activities such as social singing; further support for the hypothesis that food is not short during the winter is given by the frequent occurrences of out-of-season breeding. Against this, during the breeding season, when the birds are incubating or feeding young, less time is available for obtaining their own food requirements. The result of this is that the normally cautious sparrow has to take risks in collecting food and consequently is exposed to greater danger of being caught by a predator. This is borne out by my trapping records (see Fig. 24), which show a marked increase in the trapping of adults during the breeding season. Although for the early part of their life in the nest much of the food given to the young is animal, the adults still come to the traps baited with bread in order to feed themselves. Another factor that may be of importance is the difference in food-seeking behaviour imposed by breeding, so that the protection that is given by social feeding methods is lost in the more individual technique that has to be used in collecting insects. In addition, the severe physical strain of rearing two or three broods in quick succession may itself render the adults more liable to mortality from one of the various causes.

Food shortage, if it does occur in the life of the sparrow, probably occurs at the height of the breeding season when the population is at its maximum and competition for food may well be greatest, particularly as the young in their first few weeks of life do not move very far from their birthplaces. Admittedly the food supply at this time of year is augmented by ripening grass and weed seeds but it probably does not reach its height until the ripening of grain, which does not occur until the breeding season is almost over.

In conclusion it might be of interest to translate the survival rates given earlier in the chapter into figures of the expectation of further life, which are probably the more familiar concept. For the young birds a month old with a survival rate of twelve per cent, the expectation of further life is only seven and a half months; by their first December, however, it has increased to one and three quarter years. This is the overall figure for the adults and thus the birds can be said to be adult at this stage. There is no definite evidence of birds breeding more than five seasons, though occasional individuals live longer than this in the wild.

CHAPTER 14

NUMBERS AND DENSITY

WE HAVE seen some of the causes of death in house sparrows and have considered how long they can expect to live; this leads us logically on to a study of numbers. How common is the house sparrow? Our immediate impression is that it is one of the commonest birds, but as urban dwellers we must not be misled into exaggerating the numbers of an urban-living animal. It is of course impossible to do a complete count of the numbers of a wild animal unless it is nearing extinction or it is very conspicuous and resorts to a few selected spots for breeding. The best we can do is to obtain typical densities for different types of habitat and use these to estimate the population.

Except in a few selected cases the house sparrow does not breed away from man. It breeds on man's houses or in trees close to these; hence one key feature of its habitat is the density of buildings. Another feature of significance is the presence of cereal cultivation; it was through this that the house sparrow must first of all have become attached to man and although it is no longer an essential factor it still plays an important part, as the late summer flocks to the grain fields witness. The easiest way to consider different house sparrow habitats is in terms of the density of buildings, going from completely built-up urban areas with little open ground, through suburban areas with a much greater proportion of open ground to rural areas where building is much less a significant feature of the habitat. In the latter, the type of land and the economy must also be considered; arable compared with pasture, chicken and pig farming with cattle and sheep, farmland versus moorland.

The size of the sample area necessary is determined by the animal being studied, with wide-ranging species it must be large enough to be representative; with small sedentary species, a few acres are all that may be necessary, though the larger the area in which a count can be made the more representative will be the result obtained, provided it consists of only one habitat type. The house sparrow is extremely sedentary and, though small, it is conspicuous and easy to count, particularly during the breeding season when the birds are grouped into colonies and the nest sites can readily be located. A considerable number of censuses of house sparrows have been made and from these we can obtain a reasonable insight into the influence of habitat on population density.

The census results available from different parts of Great Britain are collected in Table 19. Most of these are for the breeding season but a few obtained in the winter are included after adjustment as indicated in the notes below the Table to give probable breeding density figures. The results are grouped into the three major habitat types: urban, suburban and rural. The Land Utilisation Survey produced by L. D. Stamp in 1948 gives the

TABLE 19

Breeding Densities of House Sparrows in Great Britain

Type of habitat	Place	Acreage	Density birds/acre
Urban:			
(1) mainly built-up (i)	London-Bloomsbury 1950	42	4·3
(2) ,, ,,	London-Lambeth 1950	—	4·0
(3) houses bordering city park	Kensington 1925–6		3 (i)
	,, 1948–9		1 (i)
Suburban:			
(1) houses and gardens	Glasgow 1959	20	2
(2) 50% houses and gardens	Stockton/Tees	234	1
50% permanent grass	1955		
Rural:			
(1) 15% houses and gardens	Harlington,	618	0·2
85% orchards and small-holdings	Middlesex 1948		

(i) These refer to feeding and not breeding areas. S. Cramp has suggested to me that the breeding area of the Kensington Gardens' birds probably lies within 50–100 yards of the Gardens. This has been used in calculating the breeding density with an adjustment made to allow for the mortality between the census date and the breeding season.

Type of habitat	Place	Acreage	Density birds/acre
Rural:			
(2) 10% houses and gardens 90% farmland (mainly dairy) and woods	N. Hampshire 1953	1280	0·5
(3) 5% houses and gardens 95% grassland	Hilbre Island, Cheshire, 1952–7	11	0·5 to 1
(4) 1% houses and gardens 1% woodland 3% allotments 95% grassland	W. Bromwich, Warwicks, 1952	3000	0·03
(5)	Ayrshire	c. 20	0·5
(6) mainly rough grazing	Ailsa Craig 1930–40	225	0·13
(7) ,, ,, ,,	Bardsey Island 1934 1952	444	0·36 (ii) 0·09
(8) ,, ,, ,,	Fair Isle 1920	3840	0·21
(9) ,, ,, ,,	Isle of May 1926–46	126	0·1
(10) ,, ,, ,,	Lundy 1939	1047	0·08
(11) ,, ,, ,,	Sanda 1951	600	0·15

(ii) Adjusted to allow for mortality between census dates and breeding season.

distribution of different categories of land in Great Britain, which, with the different densities suggested by the census results, enables us to make an estimate of the house sparrow population. This is done in Table 20. A density of two birds per acre is considered as representative of built-up areas. The rural areas where censuses have been carried out unfortunately do not include much arable land where densities might be expected to be higher; on the other hand the human population, as represented by the number of houses, is probably higher than typical for this habitat and hence it seems safer to adopt the conservative figure of 0·1 birds per acre for this environment. No census data are available for true rough grazing areas such as the Pennines or Scottish highlands; observations in these areas indicate it is lower than for farmland areas and a density of 0·01 birds per acre is suggested: fortunately the total number of birds from this habitat does not have much effect on the total population. The final category of woodland and inland waters does not support any house sparrows.

These densities give us a total population for Great Britain of about nine and a half million; if correct, this must place the house sparrow as one of the commonest species of land birds in Britain, comparable in numbers with the blackbird and chaffinch.

TABLE 20

House Sparrow population in Great Britain

Type of land	Acreage	Number of house sparrows per acre	Total number of house sparrows
Urban and suburban	3,119,000	2	6,240,000
Arable and permanent grassland	31,397,000	0·1	3,140,000
Moorland, heathland and rough grazing	18,775,000	0·01	188,000
Woodland and inland water	3,219,000	0	—
Total	56,510,000		9,568,000

Some census data that are available from other parts of the house sparrow's range are given in Table 21. It is interesting to see that in most cases the densities are similar to the British ones. The combination of a dense human population and intensive arable farmland in south Germany shows this to be as favoured a habitat for the bird as the completely built-up areas. In this type of country the sparrow becomes a pest of agriculture. In Finland, on the other hand, with extensive forest areas that are quite unsuitable for house sparrows, the population is comparatively low.

TABLE 21

Breeding Densities of House Sparrows outside Great Britain

Locality	Acreage	Density birds/acre
Finland—whole country	84,800,000	0·01
Germany—Filder Plain, S.E. of Stuttgart. Intensively cultivated area, 10% houses	1,670	2·5 to 3·0 (i)
—Kiel (built-up area)	—	2 (ii)
—Heligoland	150	0·25
Sweden—small town 50 km. from Stockholm	—	1·2 (ii)
Turkestan—agricultural village area	3,840	0·75
U.S.A.—Pennsylvania 1899–1901	640	0·33
1914		0·19
—Illinois—whole state	35,886,500	0·1 (ii)
North America—U.S.A.; part of Canada and Mexico	2,500,000,000	0·06

(i) The density is calculated from the figures given by F. Preiser before large-scale poisonings was carried out in the area; it has been adjusted to allow for mortality between the time of the census and the start of breeding.

(ii) The figures have been adjusted to allow for the mortality between the census and the start of breeding.

The results of the population studies suggest a close correlation between house sparrow and human numbers and the comparison that is made in Table 22 shows this to be the case. The estimate for the Illinois population was made in 1914 and there is a good body of evidence to suggest that numbers have diminished considerably in the eastern United States since about 1920; this would bring the ratio more in line with those from Great Britain and Finland.

TABLE 22

Comparison of Human and House Sparrow Populations

Locality	House sparrow population	Human population	Ratio House sparrows:man
Great Britain	9,568,000	50,057,000	0·19
Finland	1,000,000	4,356,000	0·23
U.S.A. (Illinois)	3,440,000	9,361,000	0·37

A number of writers have suggested that a better correlation would be obtained with the number of domestic animals, particularly chickens, horses and pigs, than directly with human population. I do not consider that this is necessarily the case. In addition to the food gleaned by the sparrow from the feed of domestic animals, man himself is a great, deliberate provider of food for small birds, much of which is eaten by sparrows. H. Sick also considers that in Brazil the introduced house sparrows are much more closely associated with man than with his cereal crops or domesticated animals.

Populations are by no means stable things and even in recent times a number of changes in densities of house sparrows have been reported, quite apart from the extensions of range that have taken place as I shall show in a later chapter. It is of interest to look closely at any changes that have occurred as these give us an insight into the requirements of the bird, though any report of a change in numbers must be treated with caution unless supported by numerical evidence; in addition, observations must be made over a considerable number of years to distinguish between the temporary effect of a widespread epidemic, such as we saw in an earlier chapter occurred in Shetland in 1926–7 and in southern France in 1915–16, and a permanent change brought about by an alteration in the habitat; for example, the occupation of the Sinai Desert by troops in the first world war modified this habitat so that it became suitable for house sparrows and they quickly moved in.

The most striking change that has been recorded is the decrease that has taken place in certain parts of the eastern half of the United States and Canada mainly during the period from 1910 to 1930. This is supported by quantitative results obtained from Massachusetts by W. F. Eaton, who found that the average number of house sparrows he saw each day decreased from 13·7 in 1914 to 5·6 in 1922, whereas there was no significant change in the numbers of three other indigenous species. Numerous other observers have reported a similar state of affairs, though without quantitative details; however it is clear, by considering the information given by W. B. Barrows in his monumental survey of the sparrow in the United States, that the population in the east of the country was very much higher than it is now, and in fact probably very much denser than anything we have known in Great Britain, though it is possible that it has not yet reached its peak in the west. The same thing has been reported for the eastern Canadian cities by R. L. Weaver and P. A. Taverner, though the population appears to have been more stable in the country districts. A similar decrease in sparrow numbers appears to have occurred in New Zealand in the early twenties, though the population is now said to be steady at the reduced level. It has been widely suggested that this decrease, which, it is claimed, was more pronounced in the towns than in country districts, can be associated with the replacement of the horse by the automobile as a means of transport; not only has this removed a great source of food from the sparrow— grain spilled from nosebags and partially digested in the droppings —but the faster moving traffic has made the streets less safe to feed in and is responsible for a considerable mortality of young birds. While this is no doubt perfectly true, I think that to some extent the decrease coincided with the natural adjustment of an intro- duced species to its environment. If birds are introduced without predators, parasites or disease organisms, the temporary absence of checks may give an abnormal increase until these catch up or native organisms adapt themselves. The decreased infantile mortality that occurs during the period of rapid expansion may mean that there is some weakening in the resistance of the stock to disease so that when disease arrives it has a more pronounced effect than it has on a more stable population. Another factor may be the increase of mechanical harvesting methods and more efficient threshing techniques that have resulted in less spilled grain that the sparrows can glean from the fields after they have been harvested; also there has probably been a decrease in the habit of keeping a few hens about the house, a practice that helped to provide a regular supply of food throughout the year for the sparrows.

There is no doubt that the decrease in the horse population has had some effect and this is almost certainly one factor in the change in the Kensington Gardens population between 1925 and 1948 as shown in Table 19. However, a contributory cause has probably been the de-population of the centres of large cities, which are now predominantly non-residential in character. This is probably responsible for the decrease in the house sparrow population of central London that still appears to be going on. A similar story comes from Chicago where A. L. Rand reports that the house sparrow is now completely absent from the "Loop", a business section where there are no yards or open spaces. Even in 1938 C. B. Ticehurst and H. Whistler reported that the sparrow was absent as a breeding species from the centre of the city of Algiers, though they came in at night to roost in the trees.

On the outskirts of towns the picture is very different. Table 19 suggests that house sparrow densities are higher in suburban than most rural areas; hence the spread of suburbs is likely to benefit the sparrow. In Great Britain alone, 100,000 acres of agricultural land has been lost to building on the average each year since the war. Observations in extending suburbs, trading estates and the New Towns clearly show that an increase in density does occur with the change in land usage. This must be taking place over most of the house sparrow's range. B. Rademacher says that both house and tree sparrows, but especially the house sparrow, have increased in the towns and occupied settlements (of Germany) to an alarming extent.

It is interesting to go back seventy to eighty years and find that writers were then remarking on the striking and deplorable increase of the house sparrow. This was attributed to the decrease in the popularity of "Sparrow Clubs" that had been responsible for killing numbers of sparrows. However, many of these were probably the surplus that would have died in any case by more natural causes and I feel that the real cause was more probably a change in agriculture or the increase in urban development.

One well documented change that has taken place is the decrease on a number of islands round the coast of Britain. Table 19 shows a fall to a quarter on Bardsey Island between 1934 and 1952; in this period the human population fell in the same proportion. A decrease in the human population on Rathlin Island has similarly resulted in a fall in sparrow numbers. On islands that have been evacuated the sparrows have quickly died out completely— Inishkea, Mayo; Great Blasket, Co. Kerry and South Havra, Shetland, may be cited as examples.

More interesting is the way that breeding populations have died out on the Isle of May and Hilbre Island without changes in the human population having taken place. On the former approximately six pairs bred from 1927–47, then the resident horse was removed from the island and the birds died out. On Hilbre the removal of the horse and poultry at the beginning of the 1956 breeding season had no immediate effect on the sparrow population or the numbers of young reared, but the population crashed during the following winter and although the remaining three pairs had a successful breeding season in 1957 the numbers fell further during the following winter and no breeding has taken place since then. Here the birds appeared to be independent of man in the summer but relied on food put out for the domestic animals to carry them through the winter months.

Although changes in numbers have taken place and indeed occur all the time as the animal adapts itself to changes in the environment, in the greater part of its range the population is essentially stable. For example, in the five years in which the population study given in Table 18, Chapter 13, is based, the number of breeding adults was sixty-two, sixty-three, seventy-eight, sixty-nine and sixty-four respectively; an annual variation probably typical of much larger areas. Population control of this sort depends on the operation of density-dependent factors, such as food supply, competition for nest sites or disease. Density-dependent (epidemic) disease would be expected to act violently, causing much greater fluctuations in numbers than is shown by observation to be normally the case. Competition for nest sites does not appear to be an important factor in most parts of the bird's range, though in a study of house sparrows at Cornell University, New York State, R. L. Weaver considered that the breeding population was limited by the availability of nest-sites, different pairs using the same site in succession. These observations appear to have been made in an area where food supplies in the winter built up a population greatly in excess of the nesting opportunities. This is not typical of the bird in America—H. Brackbill, who has made observations on colour-ringed house sparrows at Baltimore, Md., informs me that pairs retained their nests and would rear up to three broods in them during the year—and has not been recorded from other parts of the bird's range. Thus we are led to the conclusion that food is the ultimate factor in control, as has been demonstrated by D. Lack for most species of birds and as was indeed implicit in the paragraph describing the house sparrow's habitat.

Although we can see that numbers are adjusted to the food supply, it is difficult to see how this operates and how the level of population is determined, though Preiser's results discussed in Chapter 11 show how the numbers are maintained from year to year at their optimum level. For instance, it can be appreciated in a general way why sparrows are approximately twenty times more numerous in urban than in grassland areas, but it is much more difficult to see why the density in the urban areas is about two birds per acre and not twenty or 0·2. Food certainly appears to act as a density-dependent factor in controlling the increase of numbers during the breeding season. When the population pressure is reduced, as it was in the United States and other areas to which the bird was introduced, the build-up in numbers was very rapid; for example, in Topeka, Kansas, where the bird was released in 1864, a fivefold increase in numbers was recorded annually for the first few years. This could only have occurred if the juvenile mortality was temporarily reduced. Variation in juvenile mortality with population changes caused by disease, poisoning and other catastrophes is the buffer that acts to stabilise numbers.

Food supply cannot, however, be the proximate factor controlling the number of breeding pairs. That there is some regulation of breeding numbers is shown by the way the birds tend to form breeding colonies and leave apparently suitable areas unoccupied and also by the fact that in these breeding colonies there are a number of non-breeding birds of each sex. The existence of these birds is shown by colour-ringing and also by the observation that if a breeding bird of either sex dies during the breeding season its place is quickly filled from the reservoir of non-breeders. J. H. Clark gives an example in America where the successive mates of a male were shot on 25th March, 3rd April, 17th April, and 19th May; he seemed to have no difficulty each time in acquiring a new mate and, in fact, only eight days after the fourth had been killed, he was again paired and already had a nest with five eggs. This shows that these birds are capable of breeding yet they do not pair up amongst themselves and breed. Control could be exercised through behaviour patterns that have been evolved to limit the size of breeding colonies, but how these operate in a species that is not territorial in its behaviour is obscure.

CHAPTER 15

ORIGINS AND DISTRIBUTION

THE SPARROWS are thick-billed, mainly seed-eating birds and, except for recent introductions by man, are confined to Africa, Europe and Asia. Their classification has for a long time been a matter for dispute, and opinions have differed on whether they belong to the weaver-birds (Ploceidae) or the finches (Fringillidae). A careful examination of their morphology and behaviour strongly suggests their affinity to the weavers and this view is held by most modern authorities. They resemble the weavers in the structure of the horny palate and they undergo a complete juvenile moult at the age of two or three months, whereas this moult in the finches is only partial. They build typically a domed nest of grass with a side entrance, similar to that of the weavers and quite unlike the open-topped nests of the finches. Divergence from the weavers is shown by the frequent use of holes as nesting sites, a habit not practised by any other Ploceids; however, in these situations the nest is still domed, suggesting that the habit has been comparatively recently acquired. The use of holes is by no means a constant feature and, in any case, is no point of affinity with the finches. In addition, their calls and social habits are typical of the weavers. One characteristic in which they resemble the finches is the reduction in size of the outermost primary, which in the latter family is very small and externally invisible; this, in the face of the other evidence to the contrary, must clearly be a case of convergence rather than of true relationship.

Passerinae, the sub-family of Ploceidae to which *Passer* belongs, includes, in addition, five small genera confined to Africa (see Appendix 1) and two genera with more widespread distributions: *Petronia*, the rock or bush sparrows, are mainly confined to Africa, but one species occurs in southern Europe and Asia as well and two others occur in southern Asia as well as in Africa; *Montifringilla*, the snow finches, includes seven species, which occur in mountainous regions from the Pyrenees to Mongolia and are not found in Africa. In *Passer* and *Montifringilla* there is a seasonal change in the bill colour of the male: in the breeding season it is black, in the non-breeding season horn-coloured.

There are fifteen species in the genus *Passer;* six of these occur in tropical Africa, two with outliers in western Asia; a further species occurs with a very restricted distribution in the latter area; three occur widely distributed over the palaearctic region; four are confined to southern and south-east Asia, and the final species is restricted to South Africa. The distribution of the genus (see Fig. 36, pp. 245-7) suggests an origin in tropical Africa and this is supported by the fact that all of its members build a domed nest, a characteristic of tropical species.

The members of the genus of true sparrows,* *Passer*, have in common this domed, rather untidy nest built of grasses and lined with feathers, the use of trees for nesting—either in holes or in the branches—and a diet largely based on seeds, particularly those of grasses, rushes and, of course, cereals; that is they are predominantly ground feeders but tree nesters. This suggests an ancestral habitat of forest edges and scattered trees (savannah) rather than deep forest or open steppe. There has been some radiation from this: the desert sparrow (*simplex*) and saxaul sparrow (*ammodendri*) into arid regions; the Spanish sparrow (*hispaniolensis*), scrub sparrow (*moabiticus*) and Sind jungle sparrow (*pyrrhonotus*) into water-rich bush country; the house sparrow and to a lesser extent tree (*montanus*), grey (*griseus*), rufous (*iagoensis*) and Cape sparrows (*melanurus*) into cultivated land with habitations and even in the case of the house sparrow into completely built-up areas. There is a widespread tendency among the family to associate with man and at least eight of the species have been recorded breeding in the eaves of inhabited dwellings, though without exception the birds can fairly be described as wary.

Within the genus we can pick out a number of groups or subgenera in which the species more closely resemble each other. The house sparrow belongs to a palaearctic and oriental group of three

---

* The so-called sparrows of North America are unrelated; they are buntings, belonging to the family Emberizidae.

species (*domesticus, hispaniolensis, montanus*), which are similar to the African *iagoensis* not only in the head pattern and black bib but also in behaviour, being conspicuous, social at all times of the year and regularly associating with man. With the exception of *montanus*, these species are sexually dimorphic, the females resembling each other closely; in *montanus* the hen has adopted the male pattern. *Pyrrhonotus* and *moabiticus* occur in similar habitats and are much shyer birds; their present very restricted distributions suggest they are relict populations of a species that formerly was much more widely distributed. *Flaveolus* might also be of this group, though, unlike the other two, it tends to be a dry country bird. *Iagoensis* may be at present undergoing a similar contraction in Africa; some authorities in fact give specific rank to the five isolated populations of this species shown in Fig. 36:*8*, p. 246. The chestnut and golden sparrows are another closely related pair, being more birds of open country than the other members of the genus.

I suggest that the ancestral sparrow was a bird of the *griseus* type living in tropical Africa, probably a builder of bulky, untidy, domed nests of dried grass in the branches of trees and bushes. From this the black-throated birds evolved and spread down the Nile into the palaearctic region, probably in the Pliocene or late Miocene period about ten to twenty million years ago. Some of these birds spread right across southern Asia to the Far East giving rise to *pyrrhonotus* and *montanus*, others to the north and west to form *domesticus* and *hispaniolensis*. Much of this is pure speculation but largely as a result of the extensive investigations of the distribution of the sparrows round the Mediterranean region by W. Meise the picture of the evolution of the house sparrow is much clearer and it is possible to advance a more soundly based hypothesis.

Fig. 25, opposite, shows the present distribution of house and Spanish sparrows in the Mediterranean area. This distribution is a very complex one, but its very complexity gives a great opportunity of unravelling the way the present situation has arisen. To the north of the Mediterranean the house and Spanish sparrows live side by side as good sympatric species in Spain and the Balkans. The same situation holds in western north Africa but in Algeria the two species interbreed quite freely and a complete range of hybrids exists; further east in Tunisia the influence of *domesticus* dies out and only pure *hispaniolensis* occurs, though the situation is by no means stabilised and an eastward *domesticus* gene-flow seems to be taking place. In Italy neither pure typical house nor Spanish sparrows are found; instead there is a sparrow that has been named a separate species, the Italian sparrow (*P. italiae*). However, at the extreme north of Italy there is a narrow region in the southern

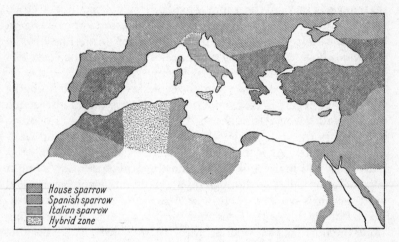

House sparrow
Spanish sparrow
Italian sparrow
Hybrid zone

FIG. 25. Present distribution of sparrows in the Mediterranean region. (After W. Meise.)

foothills of the Alps where *domesticus* and *italiae* interbreed and similarly in the extreme south of Italy and in Sicily, *italiae* and *hispaniolensis* form intermediates. The sparrows living on Pantelleria, Malta and Sardinia are predominantly *hispaniolensis;* those on Corsica are nearer to *domesticus*. Clearly *italiae* is a stabilised hybrid form between *domesticus* and *hispaniolensis* and cannot be recognised as a good species; it is purely a matter of nomenclatural convenience whether it is placed as a sub-species of *domesticus* or *hispaniolensis*—I prefer to put it with *domesticus* as in Italy it takes over the role of the house sparrow. The birds on Crete are *italiae*, but those on Scarpanto and Rhodes are intermediate between *italiae* and *domesticus*. *Italiae* shows something of its *hispaniolensis* blood in that it is less completely associated with man than other European house sparrows and breeding colonies are found away from man's dwellings both in Italy and Crete. It is interesting to notice that at the limit of the sparrow's range in Africa (Tuggurt 33° 13' N. 5° 59' E., Wargla 31° 55' N. 5° 27' E.) populations of birds that were once separated as *flückigeri;* occur at isolated oases these are rather similar to *italiae* and are almost certainly hybrids that have arisen in the same way and have become stabilised through isolation. In Cirenaica and Egypt *domesticus* appears again but *hispaniolensis* does not occur as a breeding bird. The hens of *domesticus, italiae* and *hispaniolensis* are not separable; the cocks can be compared in Plates 19 and 20, pp. 192-3.

How can the present situation be explained? The most probable sequence of events is that some of the sparrows that had reached the Nile valley from Africa began, during the Pleistocene (1,000,000 to 20,000 years ago), to spread northwards into Europe and west-wards along the African Mediterranean coast. At this time this latter area was moist and humid and the birds spreading along it became adapted to a damp habitat. This movement continued until the birds reached north-west Africa and then turned north-wards into Spain. At the same time the other group were spreading along the north of the Mediterranean. These birds, which became adapted to a rather drier habitat, joined up again with the others in Italy, which they had reached, either from Spain or across the Mediterranean via Sicily. Although the two groups had been evolving along different lines they had not differentiated enough to remain ecologically or genetically isolated and when they met again began to interbreed. It is probable that similar hybrid populations were produced in the same way in Corsica to the west and Greece and Crete to the east. This probably occurred between the third and fourth main glaciations of the Pleistocene but before more extensive mixing took place there was another glaciation that not only inhibited further spreading but cut off the existing populations in Spain and Italy from each other and the birds in the Balkans and Near East. When the ice retreated the different populations began to spread again but before they met up with each other a new and important change had taken place—the evolution of sedentary, agricultural man, probably in the south Caspian or Tigris-Euphrates region. The seed-eating sparrows in this area must have become closely associated with him and his cereal crops. With the recession of the ice, the house sparrow, for now it can be called this, began to re-colonise Europe in close association with sedentary man. The *italiae* birds in Greece were presumably absorbed by the advancing wave of *domesticus*, but this has been prevented in Italy, Crete and Corsica by their geographical isolation. Zones of intergradation between *italiae* and *domesticus* in the southern foothills of the Alps and on Rhodes and Scarpanto (also between *hispaniolensis* and *italiae* in Sicily and the extreme south of Italy) do occur; these zones are narrow, as is usually the case when the two blending forms are highly differentiated. Each of these forms has evolved nicely balanced gene-complexes, well adapted to the local conditions, and are more viable than the hybrids between them. In this advance the *domesticus* birds reached Spain but by now they and the sparrows already there (*hispaniolensis*) had differentiated sufficiently that they no longer interbred and existed as good, ecologically-separated species. The only sparrows in Sardinia are pure *hispaniolensis* type; presumably there was no penetration there of the birds from the east in their first advance and, being geographically isolated, *domesticus* has not been able to establish itself there in competition with such a close relative as *hispaniolensis* since then.

During the period of the retreat of the ice in Europe and the advance of the sparrow, the north coast of Africa gradually became increasingly arid and unsuitable for the Spanish sparrow, which became restricted to the north-west of Africa and cut off from the Egyptian birds. The house sparrow continued its spread through Spain and reached north Africa across the Mediterranean. However, when it reached Algeria it met Spanish sparrows that owing to the desiccation of this region had been forced into the biotope to which the house sparrow had become adapted and thus the two birds, still closely related, again interbred in the absence of ecological isolation. This population is much less geographically isolated than the Italian one and because of this is by no means as morphologically stable, except in the isolated oases in the south where the so-called *flückigeri* birds occur. The final episode in this story is the spread of the Spanish sparrow eastwards across southern Europe, Asia Minor and the south Caspian region to Turkestan and northern Pakistan, where it is found to-day in a zone from 30° to 40°N., predominantly a bird of water-rich bush regions as indicated by its German names: *Weidensperling* (willow sparrow) and *Sumpfsperling* (swamp sparrow). In fact with increasing aridity in Spain the bird has become rather scarce there and very local in distribution. The Spanish sparrow is principally a tree nester, both openly in trees and in the walls of the nests of large birds, such as herons and birds of prey; it is more social than the house sparrow and in parts of its range occurs in enormous colonies—W. Makatsch recorded a colony of about three hundred nests in a bramble thicket in Greece, and O. Salvin a colony of about one hundred pairs in five or six trees in the Atlas mountains; as many as twenty nests have been reported in the walls of one stork's nest. In Tripolitania and eastern Tunisia, where the house sparrow is lacking, the Spanish sparrow has taken over the "house sparrow" niche, nesting on houses, as do the hybrid populations in Malta and eastern Algeria. Also in the Canary and Cape Verde Islands, to which the Spanish sparrow has been introduced and where the house sparrow is lacking, it behaves more as a "house sparrow."

We are now in a position to consider the present distribution of the house sparrow. The major step of associating with sedentary man and his grain crops taken, the sparrow began to spread with man reaching eastwards in southern Asia to India and Burma and northwards through Europe, beginning this latter move probably about five thousand years ago. At some stage the Asian and European birds appear to have become isolated from each other, for to-day C. Vaurie points out that the various sub-species fall into two groups: the *indicus* group, which are generally smaller and white-cheeked, and the *domesticus* group, which are larger and grey-cheeked. *Indicus* birds are now found in southern Asia, Arabia and the Nile south of Dongola, probably having reached there by a secondary spread from India.

The timing of the spread into Europe is not clear and is, in fact, still taking place to-day. We cannot be certain when it first reached the British Isles, though it was probably well established by Roman times. The following passage that has been attributed to the Venerable Bede suggests that it was a familiar bird in Northumberland at the beginning of the 7th Century: "So seems the life of man, O King, as a sparrow's flight through the hall when you are sitting at meat in winter-tide, with the warm fire lighted on the hearth, but the icy rainstorm without. The sparrow flies in at one door, and tarries for a moment in the light and heat of the hearth-fire, and then flying forth from the other into the wintry darkness whence it came. So tarries for a moment the life of man in our sight, but what is before it, what after it, we know not." Certainly it was to be found all over the British Isles, including Orkney and Shetland, by the end of the 17th Century, though still locally distributed in the west and in parts of Scotland.

The period up to 1800 was one of consolidation and increase in numbers through most of Europe and southern Asia east to India. The distribution at that time is probably as shown in Fig. 26, p. 168. Since then a most remarkable change has taken place and the house sparrow has now become almost certainly the most widespread species of land bird in the world. There have been two major causes for the great increase in range that has taken place in the past century and a half: the development of agriculture and communications in Siberia and the colonisation of much of the world by man from western Europe and the subsequent introduction of the house sparrow, along with other exotic species, into these parts.

Even in the British Isles and western Europe there has been an extension of range since 1800. During the 19th Century the bird increased in numbers in Scotland and it began to appear at many of the more isolated communities where previously it had been unknown. The spread to the Western Isles has been comparatively recent. For example, it did not appear on Tiree until 1892, Coll until 1899 and, similarly, Canna was only colonised within recent memory. The earliest record for the Outer Hebrides is at Stornoway on Lewis in 1833 but it apparently died out again as it was not found in 1841, though it was common there by 1871. At the other

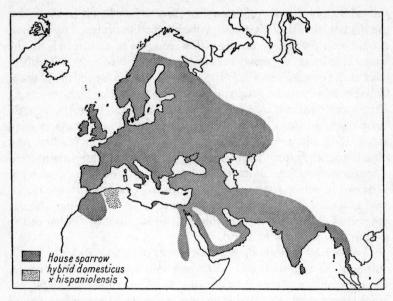

House sparrow
hybrid domesticus
x hispaniolensis

FIG. 26. World distribution of house sparrow at the beginning of the 19th
Century.

end of the Long Island it was breeding on Barra in 1837; there are
further records for 1870 and 1895, though whether it bred there
continuously is not known. The rest of the Outer Isles were
occupied only slowly; they were breeding at the north of Lewis by
1888, but the only place occupied on Harris in 1902 was Tarbert.
Not until 1913 was it reported from North Uist. There is an early
record for South Uist in 1841; and although it could not be found
in 1907 it was well established on the island by 1923. Even as late
as the early '30's it was said to be uncommon on Benbecula; in 1955
I found it present at almost every homestead on the Uists and
Benbecula and on the inhabited islands lying round the coasts. It
has never bred on St. Kilda though the tree sparrow was present
there until the island was evacuated in 1930. It was not until May
1958 that a house sparrow was first recorded.

Further to the north the house sparrow is now well established in the Faroes. There is an isolated record for Nolsö for 24th May, 1900, but it was not until 1934 or 1935 that a party arrived on Suduroy, the southernmost island of the group; almost certainly these birds travelled as passengers on a ship—the nearest breeding station being about two hundred miles to the south-east in Shetland. It arrived on Swinoy, in the northern group, about 1944; two years later it was breeding in Torshavn the capital, and was spreading over the other islands. G. R. Potts, who spent several months in the summer of 1960 on the Faroes, found it common in the towns on Suduroy, Streymoy and Vagur and it was even breeding on Mykines in the extreme west of the group; it had apparently reached there in 1953 or 1954.* In these northern towns, which are on the sea, the sparrow appears to spend a lot of its time feeding on the foreshore, as indeed they do in many of the British coastal towns. Sparrows have not yet appeared on Iceland, though there is an isolated record from Jan Mayen.

In the extreme west of Wales in Caernarvonshire and Pembrokeshire it does not appear to be common; it is surprisingly absent from some villages and small towns, though it breeds on the inhabited islands off the coast. It bred on Lundy in the Bristol Channel until the birds were exterminated at the beginning of the last war and, although odd birds have turned up there from time to time since then, it has not yet managed to re-establish itself.

Again on the west coast of Ireland it is rather uncommon and local and according to R. F. Ruttledge has even decreased in numbers between 1924 and 1938. It has been suggested that this may be a result of the replacement of thatch by slated roofs with a consequent reduction in the available number of nest-sites. It is difficult to see why this should have resulted in a decrease in Ireland when at the same time numbers were still increasing in the west of Scotland, where similar building changes were taking place—there are few slated or corrugated-iron roofed houses in which sparrows cannot find a hole suitable for nesting. Decrease in the available food seems a more likely explanation and R. F.

* In 1961 Potts found house sparrows on twelve out of seventeen of the inhabited islands.

Ruttledge has also put forward the suggestion that the cessation of the grain trade to many of the small ports on the western seaboard of Ireland and the disuse of the granaries may have been the cause; reduction in the human population may have been a contributory factor. The house sparrow breeds on many of the inhabited islands off the Atlantic coast of Ireland, though the first records for Inishark, Co. Galway, and the Great Blasket, Co. Kerry, were only in 1956 and 1953 respectively. The Blaskets were evacuated at the end of 1953 and the house sparrow was not present in 1956; its tenure was thus less than four years. Similarly, R. F. Ruttledge tells me that when the Inishkea Islands, Co. Mayo, were evacuated the house sparrow quickly disappeared.

It seems that occupation of many of the smaller islands off the coasts of the British Isles has been largely a matter of chance and in many places the birds appear to have died out after breeding for a few years—as we saw has been the case on both the Isle of May in the Firth of Forth and on Hilbre Island in the Cheshire Dee. These small isolated colonies are clearly not fully viable units, being liable to extermination by adverse circumstances or disease; a particular case has been reported from northern Norway where a small colony bred at Kirkenes from 1908 until 1931 or 1932 and then died out. Such colonies are possibly less resistant because of inbreeding. However, despite this, there has been a gradual extension and consolidation of range to include practically all of the inhabited western islands and the house sparrow is now well established on these and likely to remain unless further evacuation by man takes place.

The origins of new colonies are interesting. It seems that a small flock must arrive together: sparrow-poor areas are unattractive to single birds—witness the short stays of recent visitors to Lundy Island, which was able to maintain a sizeable breeding colony until the birds were exterminated during the war; on the other hand a locality with its full complement also appears to be unattractive in some way—J. D. Craggs during the first five years of his study on Hilbre Island, when the sparrows were breeding and the population was presumably up to strength, noticed no arrivals of strange birds (all the island inhabitants were colour-ringed so that strangers could have been easily picked out); yet in 1959, when the breeding colony had died out, visiting sparrows were seen on no fewer than thirteen occasions.

Similarly in Scandinavia and in European Russia there has been a gradual if not dramatic spread to the more isolated northern districts in the past hundred years. In Norway the house sparrow was first reported north of the Arctic Circle in 1858 in the Salten district of Nordland Province (Bødo 67° 15′ N. 14° 30′ E.). By 1872 it was in the Lofotens and in 1879 the first record comes from Troms Province (Tromsø 69° 45′ N. 19° E.). Odd birds had been seen in the most northerly province, Finmark, in the 1850's but there are no regular records until 1887. In Sweden it was north of the Arctic Circle at Kiruna (67° 50′ N. 20° 20′ E.) as early as 1840. On the borders between Norway and Russia breeding was reported on the Murman coast at the head of Peisenfjord in 1899 and on the Norwegian side at Kirkenes (69° 40′ N. 30° E.) in 1907. It was said to be common at Archangel (64° 40′ N. 41° E.) on the south shore of the White Sea in 1882 but whether the spread to Lapland took place through Russia or up the Scandinavian peninsula is not known. Now the bird breeds regularly at several stations in Lapland, including many of the coastal towns in Nordland, Troms and Finmark in Norway; Kiruna (67° 50′ N. 20° 20′ E.) and Abisko (68° 20′ N. 18° 50′ E.) in Sweden; Ivalo (68° 40′ N. 27° 35′ E.) and Inari (68° 50′ N. 27° E.) in Finland and on the Kola peninsula, where they breed in Murmansk but not in the fishing villages on the Murman coast. The northernmost locality in which they are known to breed in Scandinavia is Oskfjord (70° 40′ N.) south of Hammerfest. There is no grain grown in these northern parts and here the sparrow must be almost completely dependent on food put out by man. H. Grote, writing in 1933, considered that the presence of horses and their fodder is most important for the survival of sparrows in this area. Many of these breeding places are very widely separated by country quite unsuitable for house sparrows and it is unlikely that the birds could have spread unaided. H. M. Lund, who has reviewed the position of the house sparrow in northern Norway, considers that they have been moved from port to port on board ship. The house sparrow winters in many of these northern towns. D. W. Snow found them in Kiruna in January 1951 and they have been recorded at a number of the other towns along the railway line to Narvik in the winter months, e.g. Gällivare (67° 7′ N. 20° 24′ E.) and Malmberget (67° 11′ N. 20° 40′ E.), where they were seen at the beginning of February 1946, and Abisko in late January 1956; further north in Norway a flock of three hundred was seen at Tromsø on 22nd January, 1954, the day after the re-appearance of the sun at that latitude. Traditionally a sheaf of corn is put out for the sparrows, which also feed on scraps put on bird-tables and seeds from horse fodder. It is never completely dark during the "long night" in Arctic Lapland for there is a period of five to six hours twilight each day, even at the solstice, when the birds are able to find food. Conditions are, however, very severe with temperatures regularly down to 0°F. and a deep cover of snow on the ground; numbers of sparrows perish during severe winters but nevertheless a breeding population appears to be able to maintain itself despite the fact that the short-ness of the breeding season permits the rearing of only one brood per pair, this testifies to the adaptability of a species which seems to be equally at home in the tropics.

Even in southern Europe there appears to have been a spread, in this region into higher altitudes that have only comparatively recently been colonised; for example, in the Pyrenees where C. B. Ticehurst and H. Whistler writing in 1927 considered that in the previous forty years it had penetrated further and further into the hills and increased.

There has also been an increase in range along the great northward-flowing rivers in Russia. In the Petchora valley they had reached 68° N. in 1880. The spread up the Ob valley began about 1800 and the bird was at Berezova (64° N.) in 1876; in 1897 it was breeding at Obdursk (Salekhad, 66° N.), probably by intro-duction of some birds from Tobolsk in 1894. The house sparrow has now reached the Yamal peninsula and odd birds had been reported from Novaya Zembla, though they do not breed there yet. In the Yenisei valley the story is similar: Worogowo (61° N.) was reached by 1840 and the Arctic Circle penetrated by 1870. It was said to be a summer visitor to Igarka (67° N.) in 1901. Much of the spread along both the Ob and the Yenisei was no doubt helped by the export of grain in barges down these rivers.

Quite the most dramatic extension of range in the palaearctic region, however, has been eastwards. The picture is not very clear, though it appears to have started on the Irtysh about 1800 when the Russians began to till the soil there; in the second half of the century the house sparrow was at Lake Baikal and by 1929 it had reached the mouth of the River Amur at Nikolaewsk. This spread has followed the growth of agriculture eastwards, the extension of the coach roads and the building of the trans-Siberian railway. It seems probable that the sparrow was helped on its way by deliberate introductions but I have been unable to find any evidence for this or more detailed information about the spread; now it extends in a narrowing belt eastwards across the whole of Siberia as well as northwards along the great river valleys. To the south it has penetrated northern Mongolia and now occurs at Ulan Bator and villages along the Selanga river; further extensions southwards have been stopped by the Gobi desert and it does not appear to have made its way yet round the eastern end of the Gobi into China.

There is no evidence to suggest that there has been much recent change in the distribution of the sparrow in the southern part of its range in the palaearctic and oriental regions. In Morocco, to the west of the *domesticus* × *hispaniolensis* mixed zone, pure house sparrows occur as we have already seen; they are found as far south as 31° N. and up to seven thousand feet in the Great Atlas. South of the mixed species region in central Algeria, pure house sparrows are again found (e.g. In Salah, 27° N. 2° 30′ E.) but in Libya they occur only in Cyrenaica, where they breed in the coastal region, other occupied places and even far out into the desert where there are trees and bushes. These birds are of the same race as the Moroccan ones (*P.d. tingitanus*). In Egypt, oddly enough, the house sparrow is absent from the Mediterranean towns to the west of the Nile delta and it breeds only along the Nile valley, where it extends as far south as 12° N. in the Sudan, and in Sinai—during the First World War the house sparrow followed the troops into Sinai and was to be seen at all the desert camps—though it appears irregularly along the Red Sea coast in autumn. In Arabia the house sparrow is found not only round the more densely populated coast but also generally throughout the central plateau and in places away from habitations. Throughout Persia, Pakistan, India and Ceylon it is a common, though in places local, resident in all inhabited parts up to eight thousand feet, but in Afghanistan, northern Pakistan, Russian Turkestan and Kashmir, as I have already mentioned, it is a summer visitor, breeding up to fifteen thousand feet in the Karkorams; these migratory house sparrows winter in the plains of north-west India and Pakistan, though a few remain in the Kashmir valley. In the steppe between the Caspian and Aral Seas these *indicus* group birds meet *domesticus* group birds from the north. There is no real zone of intergradation; this suggests that the two types have only recently made contact, possibly as a result of the *domesticus* birds spreading southwards. The house sparrow reaches southern Tibet, Nepal and Sikkim but it is absent from Bhutan; in Burma it becomes distinctly local, though it is found as far south as Rangoon. An introduction to the Andaman Islands about 1860 appears to have been unsuccessful; none were present in 1865. They reach their most southerly point in Asia at 6° N. in Ceylon.

The house sparrows of Baluchistan, Persian Baluchistan and south Afghanistan appear to be somewhat variable. Sarudny in 1903 described a new species, *Passer enigmaticus*, on the basis of two specimens from Baluchistan. These birds were very similar to female *domesticus*, though they were males. For about fifty years nothing more was heard of this species until E. Mayr, after a study of considerable house sparrow material from this area, came to the conclusion that it was incorrectly based on birds that were house sparrow intersexes. This is the meeting point of one of Vaurie's *domesticus* group sub-species (*p.d. persicus*) and two of his *indicus* group sub-species (*P.d. indicus and P.d. parkini*), one of which is a migratory race (*parkini*) and the other a sedentary one.

The present distribution in the Palaearctic region is given in Fig. 27.

The extension of range in Siberia is merely a continuation of the spread that has occurred with the continuous spread of agriculture; that is, as the habitat has changed it has become suitable for the house sparrow and the bird has moved in. The

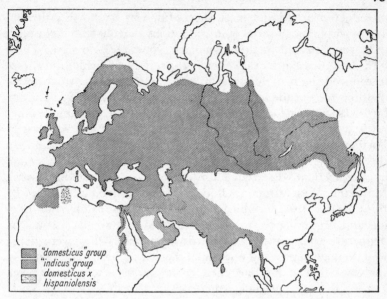

FIG. 27. Present distribution of house sparrow in Palaearctic and Oriental Regions.

second great extension that has occurred in the past hundred years is quite different in character. Here the bird was deliberately introduced into areas that had already been developed agriculturally for some time. The outstanding thing about these introductions has been their extraordinary success. The main reason for this has been the lack of competition from native species. No bird of any other genus has exploited and adopted man-made urban habitats to anything like the extent of the house sparrow and thus there were no real competitors.

These introductions were partly made for sentimental reasons— the desire of the colonists to have familiar things around them to remind them of their homelands—and partly with the hope, usually mistaken, that the sparrows would help to combat plagues of harmful insects, for example, the snow-white linden moth (*Eunomos subsignarius*) in the United States. The first of these introductions, and the most successful, was to North America. There was in fact a series of introductions starting with eight pairs that were released in Brooklyn Park, New York, in 1850. These birds had died out by the following spring but a further fifty were introduced the next year and lived to breed. Further small introductions were made to New York between 1860 and 1870 and the bird was soon well established. This was just the beginning: other birds were brought from Europe in the 1850's and released at Portland, Maine; Boston, Mass. and Peacedale, Rhode Island. In the following decade further releases were made in these states and in Connecticut, Pennsylvania (at least one thousand birds), Maryland, West Virginia, Ohio, Kentucky, Illinois and Texas. By this time the introduced birds were breeding successfully, multiplying and beginning to spread; this spread was greatly assisted by deliberate transportations of birds from places they were doing well to new areas—at one time there was such a "boom" in sparrows that it became cheaper to import them direct from Europe than to purchase American-bred birds from New York! Most of this transplanting was confined to the eastern states but some were taken to San Francisco in 1871 and others to Salt Lake City in 1873. The first Canadian record is from Quebec in 1865, again a deliberate introduction. Much of this information comes from the monumental survey of the house sparrow published by W. B. Barrows in 1889 and in his words: "From this time (1875) to the present, the marvellous rapidity of the sparrow's multiplication, the surpassing swiftness of its extension, and the prodigious size of the area it has overspread are without parallel in the history of any bird. Like a noxious weed transplanted to a fertile soil, it has taken root and become disseminated over half a continent before the significance of its presence has come to be understood. . . . We can never know how many separate introductions were made, nor how many thousands of individuals were introduced, but it is certain that the number of places thus supplied is much greater than has been supposed, and considering this fact and the rapid rate at which the sparrow breeds, we ought not to wonder that it has as completely overrun the country." By 1883, when Barrows's detailed survey of the house sparrow in the United States and

PLATE 17. Party of sparrows feeding on ripening grain. (*C. W. Teager*)

PLATE 18. Social gathering in winter hedgerow. (*C. W. Teager*)

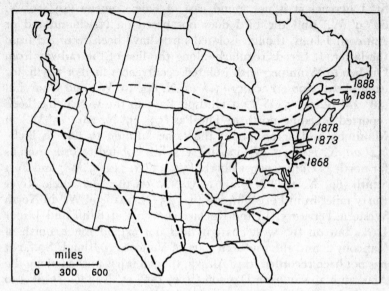

FIG. 28. Spread of house sparrow in North America. (After L. Wing.)

Canada was made, the bird was present in strength in the east, occupying about a third of the United States and part of four of the Canadian Provinces, with a few isolated introductions in the west. Figure 28, which is due to L. Wing, shows, in a general way, the extension of range in five year periods from 1868 to 1888. By 1898 it was present in all of the United States with the exception of Wyoming, Nevada, New Mexico and Arizona, Southern California (Bakersfield) and Arizona (Tucson) being reached in 1901 and 1903 respectively, but in the next few years it had spread to these, and was moving further southwards into Mexico and northwards in Canada. Most of the American birds are based on stock brought from England and, in fact, the bird is known there as the English sparrow, but some also came from Germany and possibly other European countries as well. Now in Canada house sparrows occur up to the limit of cultivation; in the east, the Gaspé peninsula and the Magdalen Islands are occupied but on the north bank of the

HS-N

St. Lawrence it is not found east of Baie Comeau (49° 10′ N. 68° 9′ W.) and the bird does not breed on Newfoundland or Anticosti Island, though isolated birds have been recorded from the latter. It breeds regularly along the line of the railway from Quebec to Winnipeg with isolated occurrences further north, for example at Moose Factory (51° 20′ N. 80° 40′ W.) and Churchill (58° 45′ N. 94° 5′ W.) on Hudson Bay; to the west it has been reported breeding north to The Pas (53° 45′ N. 101° 15′ W.) in Manitoba and across about the same latitude to Lac la Biche (54° 20′ N. 112° 10′ W.) in Alberta, with isolated records from as far north as Chipewyan, Alberta (58° 45′ N. 111° 5′ W.) and Fort Smith (60° N. 112° N.) and at 62° N. on the Mackenzie River thirty miles from Fort Simpson (61° 45′ N. 121° 30′ W.) in North Western Territory. In the Rockies it occurs at Banff and Jasper Parks but on the west coast it does not extend much north of Vancouver and the southern part of Vancouver Island. So far it has not been recorded from Alaska, though it has pushed along the Alaskan highway from Dawson Creek (55° 45′ N. 120° 15′ W.) to Fort Nelson (58° 50′ N. 122° 30′ W.).

It is not known with certainty when house sparrows first arrived in Mexico but they were present in Brownsville, Texas, in 1905, Tombstone, Arizona, in 1904 and San Diego, California, in 1913, so it is probable that the border was crossed early in this century. By 1930 they were present in Lower California and the western states as far south as Guadalajara (21° N.), in the east as far as San Luis Potosi (22° N.); by 1938 they had reached Chilpancingo (17° 30′ N. 99° 40′ W.), the capital of Guerrero State in the west and Alvarado (18° 40′ N. 95° 50′ W.) on the Gulf. In 1948 the house sparrow arrived in Tuxtla Gutierres (16° 50′ N. 93° 10′ W.), the capital of Chiapas State, lying within one hundred miles of the Guatemala border.

An introduction was made to Bermuda in 1874 and the bird is now exceedingly common there. It has still a patchy distribution in the Caribbean, though it has been there for over a hundred years. Monks brought house sparrows from Spain to Havana in 1850 and to-day the bird is distributed all over the settled parts of the island of Cuba. The next release was in Nassau, on New

FIG. 29. Present distribution of house sparrow in North America.
o irregular occurrences (most northerly).
x introduced but died out.

Providence Island, the capital of the Bahamas, in 1875, though it was reputed to have been wiped out there by a hurricane in 1909. In 1953 a small colony was established on St. Thomas, Virgin Islands, and the bird is also present in the north of Jamaica from Port Antonio to Port Maria.

In Greenland it has been less successful: sparrows were brought from Denmark to Ivigtut, a cryolite mining area north of Frederikshaab (62° N. 49° 30′ W.) in the 1880's but, though they bred for a few years, were not able to maintain themselves and died out. The present distribution in North America is given in Fig. 29.

In South America the introductions were rather later than in the north and the spread was at first less rapid, but now the bird is to be found over most of the southern half of the sub-continent, south of 15°–20° S. The first release was of about twenty pairs in Buenos Aires in 1872 in a mistaken attempt to control a harmful Psychid moth (*Oeceticus platensis*). After an introduction of this sort there is an induction period before the numbers build up and an extension of range takes place. By the end of the 19th Century the house sparrow was advancing across the border into Uruguay; since then the spread has become a positive explosion and the simple picture is confused by a mixture of unaided enterprise on the part of the birds, transplantations by the local people and further introductions from Europe, the latter coinciding with the large scale immigration of Western Europeans into Brazil, Uruguay, Argentina and Chile at the turn of the century. The chief introductions at that time were to Brazil in 1903, with the hope that it would combat a caterpillar that was attacking the ornamental shrubs that were planted during the modernisation of the capital, Rio de Janeiro, and to Santiago, Chile, in 1904. It will be interesting to see whether, after over fifty years' experience of the house sparrow, the Brazilians will be so keen to have it in their new capital, Brasilia.

Two of the transplantations that occurred once the birds became established in the places of the principal introductions were to Punta Arenas on the Magellan Straits in 1918 (probably by monks from Buenos Aires) and to Callao, Peru, in 1953. Now the gaps have been filled and in the southern part the distribution is

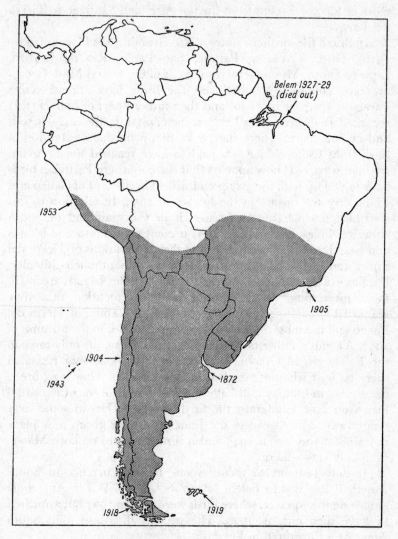

FIG. 30. Distribution of house sparrow in South America.
x principal introductions.
o later introductions or arrivals aboard ships.

more or less continuous from Buenos Aires and Santiago to Tierra del Fuego.

In Brazil the southern states of Rio Grande do Sul (occupied by 1910), Santa Caterina, Parana, Sao Paulo, Rio de Janeiro, Espirito Santo, Minas Gerais and parts of Goiaz and Mato Grosso are now colonised. In the west the birds have spread across Paraguay (present by 1920) and the southern part of Bolivia (first recorded 1928), reaching La Paz, the capital, in the early 1950's, and on into Peru, where they have met a northern extension of birds from Chile, which was said to have reached the Peruvian frontier in 1940. It now appears that these southern Peruvian birds have joined up with the group established in the area of Callao and Lima after the release in the former in 1953. In addition to this distribution over the southern half of the mainland of South America, house sparrows are now present on a number of islands and island groups round the coast; the colonisations of Tierra del Fuego and Chiloe Island probably did not present much difficulty, but those of the Falkland and the Juan Fernandez Islands are much more interesting, nevertheless it is worth mention that they reached Ushuaia (54° 50′ S. 68° 50′ W.), the capital of Tierra del Fuego and the most southerly town in the world, in the autumn of 1957. A small number of birds arrived in Stanley, the only town in the Falklands, in October or November 1919, having travelled there on four whaling vessels from Montevideo. They now breed commonly in Stanley and have spread to some of the other settlements on East Falklands, the furthest being Darwin some sixty miles away. The spread to the Juan Fernandez group took place in a similar way about 1943 and it is now present on both Mas-a-tiera and Mas-a-fuera.

It only remains to mention one final occurrence in South America: this was in Belem (1° 20′ S. 48° 30′ W.) in Amazonia almost on the equator, where birds were seen in 1927 but appeared to have died out by 1929. The present distribution in South America is illustrated in Fig. 30.

Travelling westwards the house sparrow is next to be met with in the Hawaiian Islands; it was brought there from New Zealand in 1870 or 1871 and by 1880 was said to be common in Honolulu.

To-day it is present on all of the inhabited islands in the group. Australia and New Zealand have both been colonised. The first importations to New Zealand were not successful in that few birds survived the journey from Europe, only one being released in Nelson in 1862 and two in Auckland in 1865. Larger introductions were made in the years 1866–8 to combat plagues of caterpillars and insects. It is claimed that the sparrows were of benefit to both grain growing on South Island and fruit growing on North Island, nevertheless by 1882 the birds had themselves become a plague, when they were said to be common in all settled areas and had even appeared in the most inaccessible places. It has also found its way to many of the surrounding island groups; some of these have had deliberate introductions, but in others (including Campbell Island (52° 30′ S. 169° E.) lying three hundred and fifty miles SSE. and Norfolk Island (29° 3′ S. 196° 6′ E.) lying four hundred and fifty miles NW.) the bird seems to have arrived by dispersal from the mainland by wind. It breeds on the inhabited islands but on the others its stay has usually only been temporary. Much of the introduction to New Zealand was organised through acclimatisation societies but private enterprise also played its part and in the early days as much as one pound was paid for a pair of sparrows by nostalgic immigrants.

Introductions to Australia occurred at about the same time. Large numbers were released in both Melbourne and Sydney in 1863 and, in the former at least, further releases were made at intervals up to 1872. Birds were also liberated at Launceston in Tasmania—it is said in mistake for tree sparrows—they are now plentiful there and on King and Flinders Islands lying in the Bass Strait as well. The bird has now spread to all settled areas in Victoria and New South Wales with a northward extension along the coastal region to about 23° S. in the central district of Queensland (although an attempted introduction there in 1869 apparently failed) and a westward extension to South Australia. In this state a spread has taken place northwards along the railway line to Alice Springs and although the Northern Territory has not yet been penetrated, sparrows have got at least as far as Oodnadatta (27° 30′ S.). In many parts of the world the house sparrow has been

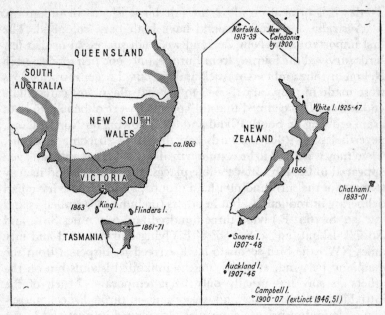

FIG. 31. Distribution of house sparrow in Australasia.
x main introductions: where known, the date of arrival is given; two dates
indicate that birds arrived during this period.

known to spread along railway lines during their construction,
by living on scraps at the railhead camps. By the time the Adelaide-
Perth railway was being built (1912–17) the attitude towards the
house sparrow had changed and a man was employed to kill any
sparrows that appeared along the line; this was done so successfully
that the sparrow was unable to penetrate into Western Australia
and legal measures were enacted to prohibit its introduction. In
the absence of the railhead camps, the distance between inhabited
places along the line across the arid and uncongenial Nullarbor
Plain is on the average fifty miles, with a maximum between
stations of seventy miles. This has been sufficient to deter the house
sparrow from making the journey. The furthest west along the line
where the sparrow occurs is Tarcoola (135° E.). Odd birds have
managed to get through, either by train or on ship (viz. a pair at

Freemantle in 1927, single bird there 1946); these were quickly destroyed and not allowed to become established. House sparrows are also present in New Caledonia; information on the precise date of introduction does not appear to be available, though they were certainly there before 1900 and to-day they are common, particularly in the European settlements. The present distribution in Australasia is given in Fig. 31.

The house sparrow is found on three Indian Ocean islands: Réunion, Mauritius and Rodriguez.* Birds of the Indian race have been present on Réunion since 1845; in Mauritius the bird was certainly present in 1885 and it is related by Col. Meinertzhagen that the population there is said to be derived from a pair brought out from England by a British soldier, who was admitted to hospital on the way to India and died on the island, the birds being liberated. Against this B. Benedict states that the Mauritius birds are of the Indian race and it may well be that they were brought there from Réunion. It does not appear to be known when they came to Rodriguez but to-day the house sparrow is ubiquitous on all of the three islands. A more recent introduction has been to Java, where it appears to have become established in some of the towns.

The bird is present on three of the four Comoro islands lying between Madagascar and the mainland of Africa. Details of the introduction are again not known, though they were on Grand Comoro by 1879 and on Moheli by 1903. These birds appear to have had an African origin as they have been identified as belonging to the sub-species *rufidorsalis*, which occurs in Sudan along the upper Nile. House sparrows are not to be found on Mayotte, but in 1943 they were brought by the occupying troops to Pamanzi, one of the neighbouring islands, where they still occupy only one village. They are said to have been introduced to Anjouan but must have died out as they are not there now. The distribution on the two islands where they have been for some time is interesting: on Moheli they are present in every village, while on the Grand

---

* According to a recent publication (1962), house sparrows are common on two of the islands of the Chagos Archipelago (6° S. 72° E.)—Peros Banhos and Salomon. No information appears to be available on the time or manner of their arrival.

Comoro they are found in only one; C. W. Benson, who recently made an expedition to the group of islands, could not detect any difference between the islands to account for this.

On the mainland of Africa introductions were made at Durban and East London about 1890. The extension of range here has been less spectacular than in other parts where it has been liberated: from Durban the house sparrow has spread over all Natal and into Transvaal and Orange Free State; from East London a spread has taken place along the coastal regions of Cape Province joining up in the north with the birds from Durban. The Natal birds are of the southern Asian sub-species *indicus*, whereas the Cape ones are of *domesticus* stock from Europe. *Indicus* birds were introduced from Bombay to Zanzibar about 1900 and are still confined to the city. It now also occurs at Mombasa, Kenya, and Berbera, British Somaliland. The distribution of the introduced house sparrows in Africa is shown in Fig. 32.

It is interesting that the house sparrow appears to have been less successful in its African introductions than in other parts of the world. Here is the one place where members of the genus *Passer* were already established: in South Africa there were *P. griseus* and *P. melanurus;* in Zanzibar, *griseus*—both of these are to some extent "house sparrows" though not so completely associated with man as *domesticus*.

One final introduction remains to be mentioned, an unsuccessful one. Twenty-six house sparrows from London were introduced to St. Helena by J. C. Mellies in November 1820 with some other British birds and although the sparrows succeeded in establishing themselves in Jamestown they apparently died out after a few years. Why it should have failed is not easy to understand, but introductions are chancy things, particularly if the numbers are small—witness the failure of the eight pairs introduced to New York in 1850, the small release in Brisbane in 1869 and the disappearance from islands round the British coast.

In a paper published a few years ago I contrasted the rate of spread with that of the fulmar. This was not a good comparison: the spread of the fulmar, although dependent upon man, took place quite unaided; the spread of the house sparrow in those countries to

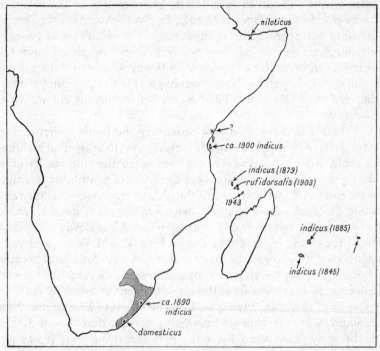

FIG. 32. Distribution of introduced house sparrows in Africa: where known the sub-species and the date of introduction are given; otherwise the date first recorded is given in parentheses.

which it was introduced was greatly helped by subsequent trans-plantations of the locally-established birds to other parts of the country. Nevertheless a considerable amount of unaided, or at least not intentionally aided, dispersal must have occurred. In North and South America the pattern of spread appears to have been very similar: first the cities and larger towns were occupied and from these the birds infiltrated to the villages and populous farming areas. The main factor responsible was most probably the transportation of grain. Certainly those towns connected by rail were first occupied; the birds may have moved in the railcars— there are a number of observations to support this—or along the lines which carried large quantities of grain and where scattered grain was usually to be found. The grain barges on the Siberian rivers played a corresponding role. In South America, the second phase of the spread, the occupation of the villages and country surrounding the towns, has not yet been completed and the distribution of the house sparrow in the areas where it does occur is still curiously patchy. Here too it has met with some competition; the roof rat (*Mus rattus*) has become an important enemy at its nesting sites.

When it is considered how sedentary the house sparrow is in most parts of its range it is not surprising that the dispersal is rather variable. This is particularly the case when the suitable habitats are separated by even quite short distances of unsuitable country, as we can see from the failure of the bird to reach western Australia along the Trans-Australian Railway. On the other hand it is able to spread over unfavourable country when this is slowly crossed by man; for example, in Egypt in the First World War, as already mentioned, it followed the army mule trains into Sinai and became abundant at all the desert camps. Extensive dispersals do occur, however, as is evident from the establishment of breeding colonies on some of the islands lying well off the coasts of Britain and New Zealand, where it appears reasonably certain that they were not deliberately introduced by man; it is surprising that it has not spread more widely in a similar way in the Caribbean area from Cuba where it has been established for over fifty years.

The success of the sparrow is even more striking when we look at the fate of other introduced bird species in different parts of the world. Attempts have been made to acclimatise something over thirty exotic species in the United States, including about twenty European passerines; of the latter only the house sparrow and starling have been at all successful, though small colonies of the tree sparrow and goldfinch still maintain themselves. Among the non-passerines, mostly game-birds, only the pheasant and partridge have managed to survive. On the other hand, eight European passerines have been able to establish themselves in the more temperate regions of Australia and twelve in New Zealand; as in North America the house sparrow and starling are the most successful and these two species appear to be the only ones from

Europe that have done at all well in South Africa. It is worth noting that the only other passerine that has been a really successful colonist is the common mynah from India and its neighbouring countries, which is now widespread in South Africa, Australia, Tasmania, New Zealand and a number of the smaller islands in the southern hemisphere—this is another species that is very closely associated with man.

It is possible to speculate on the further spread of the house sparrow that is likely to occur. In North America, the limit in the north is already the limit of cultivation and no dramatic extension is immediately likely. To the south it is probable that the bird will continue to spread southwards in Central America. In South America the main change likely in the near future is the consolidation of that area of the sub-continent already occupied. Northward extension in Brazil will probably be hindered by virgin tropical forest, except for the de-forested and settled zone on the coast. The way looks clear, however, for a further extension of range on the west coast, through Ecuador, Columbia and Venezuela to an eventual link-up with the birds from Central America.

It seems improbable, despite efforts against it, that the house sparrow will for long be denied entry to Western Australia but extensions in other parts of Australasia appear unlikely. Further spread is to be expected in South Africa despite competition from related species—none of these is as well adapted as the house sparrow to living in close association with man. The only important agricultural area in the world where the house sparrow is absent is China and Japan. Here the tree sparrow acts as the "house sparrow" but there is little doubt that if the house sparrow arrived it would displace its smaller relative from the towns. It seems unlikely that the spread from the Amur region to Manchuria and Korea and on into China proper can long be delayed. Finally a gradual extension is certain to occur in Siberia as this great area is developed agriculturally. E. Gebhardt quotes how a small party of sparrows joined a ship bound for Australia at Bremerhaven on 14th July, 1950, and did not disembark until they had arrived in Melbourne. With this ability to traverse the oceans there must be few parts of the world denied to the bird.

A final point of interest in connection with the enormous and rapid expansion in numbers of house sparrows that has taken place in different parts of the world is the possibility that, through reduced selection pressure in these areas, there would be a greater variability in characters than in established populations in long-settled parts of the bird's range. Once selection pressure had become effective again, as the population became stabilised a rapid evolution of a type most suited to the new environment might be expected. With these points in mind, D. Lack investigated groups of American specimens, from "eastern states", "mid-western states" and California, and compared them for bill length, depth of bill and wing lengths with series from England and Germany, the sources of the American birds. The interesting fact emerged that the American populations were no more variable than the European ones and, apart from a slight increase in bill size for the birds from the southern part of California and lower California, had not altered significantly in the characters measured. It should, however, be pointed out that the material available to Lack was not entirely suited to this study (most specimens were collected after the initial period of rapid increase); a new investigation of birds collected in South America where a rapid expansion is at present taking place and where climatic conditions are very different from those in the countries of origin of the birds, might give some very interesting results. This amazing stability of the house sparrow, particularly if confirmed by a more complete study, suggests that the environmental factors in the rather restricted habitat that it occupies may be substantially independent of the surrounding climatic conditions and much less variable than casual observation would lead one to expect.

This completes our story of the dramatic spread of the house sparrow: in the last hundred years its range has more than doubled and at present it occurs on about a quarter of the earth's surface, being found from 6° to 70° in the northern hemisphere and from 12° to 55° in the southern, and a wide variety of habitats from sea level up to as high as fifteen thousand feet.

CHAPTER 16

SOME ECOLOGICAL ASPECTS

ECOLOGY is the study of organisms in relation to their environment, including the way in which the whole complex of animals and plants live together. Comprehensive ecological studies have only been made in very simple, more or less isolated communities and nothing like that can be attempted for the house sparrow. While we do not know what effect, if any, the sparrow has on the species of insects it feeds to its young, what influence it has on plant life or to any real extent what role it plays as a prey for larger animals, enough is known about its relationship with one or two other species of birds to make a study of this worthwhile. The controversial field of economic ornithology—that is its relationship with man—which is apt to raise much sentiment and emotion, I shall leave for a later chapter.

Animal species are related to each other in two different ways: either in a predator-prey relationship or in competition for some necessity of life, for example, food or nest-site. The house sparrow fills the role of prey in its relations with the sparrow-hawk, tawny owl and cat; it competes with hole breeders such as starling, swift and house finch for nest-sites and drives birds like house martins, cliff swallows and fairy martins from the nests they have built and makes use of them itself. Little is known about the influence of these factors on the control of populations.

Competition is obviously greatest between closely-related species. At least eight members of the genus *Passer* nest to some extent in occupied buildings and appear to have similar food requirements, though none are as completely associated with man as the house sparrow; with only two of these, however—the Spanish and tree sparrows—is there sufficient overlap in range and habitat for competition to occur, though comparatively recent introductions have brought the house sparrow into possible contact with the Cape sparrow in Natal and the grey sparrow in Zanzibar.

It is interesting that of all its introductions the house sparrow has been least successful in South Africa. On Zanzibar Island the grey sparrows are entirely birds of the bush and show no tendency to act as "house sparrows" as they do to some extent in other parts of their range. The fascinating relationship between house and Spanish sparrows has already been described; that with the tree sparrow is equally interesting and is worthy of the same attention.

In Great Britain we normally think of the tree sparrow (Plate 20b, p. 193) as a bird of the countryside where there are scattered trees with suitable holes for nesting, possibly most particularly in moister areas, such as river valleys. In Scandinavia, however, it is a common bird of the towns, freely associating with the house sparrow, and in the Far East, where the latter species is lacking, the tree sparrow behaves as a complete "house sparrow", breeding in houses and living close to man. The tree sparrow almost certainly evolved in the oriental region from birds of the stock that gave rise to the house and Spanish sparrows in Europe. It is perhaps relevant that an independent evolution of sedentary agricultural man probably took place in the south-east of Asia and it seems possible that the tree sparrow became associated with these men in the east in the same way that the house sparrow did in the west. The association does not appear to be as strong, however, in the case of the tree sparrow, which in many parts of its range can be found breeding away from man.

As the house sparrow spread as a commensal of man from its centre in the Near East, so the tree sparrow spread northwards and westwards in Asia. It is a slightly smaller species than the house sparrow and when it came into the already established range of the latter it was only able to colonise the area successfully by adopting the more rural habitat we associate with it in Britain. In European villages, however, where the house sparrow for some reason is lacking, for example in parts of the Swiss Alps and southern Germany, it has adopted the "house sparrow" role, breeding in the roofs of houses. On St. Kilda, where the house sparrow has never bred, the tree sparrow lived in the village area, though when the island was evacuated they soon disappeared; similarly when North Rona was occupied, the breeding sparrow was *montanus*.

PLATE 19. *Above*: Male *Passer d. domesticus*: the sub-species of Europe and northern Asia, which has been introduced to many parts of the world. Note the contrast between the dark grey crown and the chestnut sides of the head. This photograph was taken in America; the introduced house sparrow is not distinguishable from the nominate race. (*Maslowski and Goodpaster*). *Below*: Male *Passer d. italiae*: the well differentiated sub-species found in Italy. In the Italian sparrow the chestnut extents completely over the crown. (*S. Frugis*)

PLATE 20. *Above*: Male *Passer hispaniolensis*: the male Spanish sparrow has a similar head pattern to the Italian sparrow, but the black bib is more extensive and the flanks heavily streaked. (*E. Hosking*). *Below*: *Passer montanus*: the tree sparrow has a chocolate crown and nape, and a black patch on the cheek; unlike the house sparrow and Spanish sparrows, the female tree sparrow has the same plumage as the male. (*E. Hosking*)

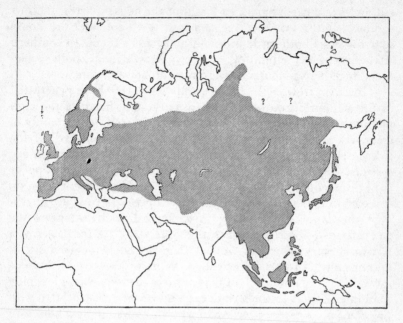

FIG. 33. Distribution of tree sparrow in Palaearctic and Oriental Regions.

The present distribution of the tree sparrow is given in Fig. 33. Much of it overlaps that of the house sparrow (see Fig. 27, p. 175), though it is not found in most of India, West Pakistan and the Near East. The most interesting region is at the junction of India, Pakistan, Afghanistan and the U.S.S.R., where the distributions of the two species begin to overlap. The tree sparrow is a resident in this area and behaves as a "house sparrow". It must have arrived from the north and occupied the domestic niche before the house sparrow appeared. The house sparrow arrived from the south and was only able to occupy this mountainous region by adopting a migratory mode of life and the tree sparrow has been able to retain its attachment to man. Not only does it maintain its role as a "house sparrow" but it actually appears to be dominant, taking up its nesting-site before the house sparrow arrives in spring and forcing the latter to nest away from houses in

HS-O

cliff holes and earth banks. In Kashmir the house sparrow is also a summer visitor but the tree sparrow is absent and the house sparrow nests both on houses and away from them. In southern Afghanistan, at the limit of the tree sparrow's range, both species breed together on houses, though they do not associate.

House sparrows of the *indicus* group (see p. 166) have penetrated to the steppes of southern Russian Turkestan, north of the high mountain ranges but they are still migratory and breed mainly in trees while *P. montanus* is the common "house sparrow" of the towns. However, in the northern part of this area sedentary *domesticus*-type house sparrows are extending their range and appear to be displacing tree sparrows from the towns. The present situation is shown in Fig. 34. In the region where house sparrows are migratory, they appear to be at a psychological disadvantage to the tree sparrow, possibly in much the same way as a trespasser of a territorial species appears to be when it enters the territory of another bird. In parts of its range the house sparrow withstands severer winter climates than that of these districts where it is only a summer visitor. In the former case, however, it is associated with the more profligate western man who provides ample food scraps throughout the winter. The tree sparrow, on the other hand, is more capable of obtaining a living on natural foods and is able to remain as a resident in these parts. In Burma, where the species again meet at the limits of their range, a delicate balance also exists; to the south and east the tree sparrow dominates and is the "house sparrow", while the house sparrow breeds in holes in river banks, to the north and west the roles are reversed. In the remainder of this region of overlap the house sparrow is completely dominant. In Britain it occasionally uses tree holes for nesting and apparently has no difficulty in driving out tree sparrows from any holes it fancies, though I have seen both species feeding young at the same time in holes in the same tree only about a foot apart.

It is interesting that the tree sparrow seems to have reached many of the northern and western parts of the British Isles before the house sparrow. However, when the latter has arrived on many of the small islands off the west coast the tree sparrow has quickly disappeared. For example, on Tiree and Coll the tree sparrow was

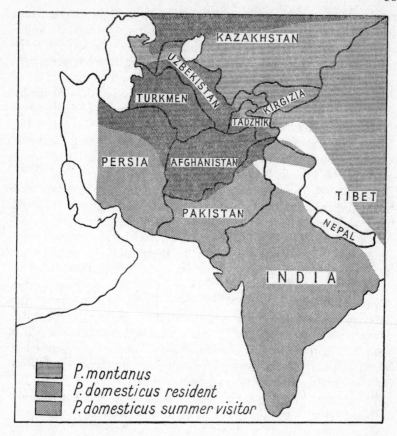

FIG. 34. Distribution of house and tree sparrows in region of overlap in central Asia.

a common breeding species before the arrival of the house sparrow in 1892 and 1899 respectively; it had disappeared from both by 1913. Similarly, it formerly bred on Eigg, Iona, Raasay, Fair Isle and the Outer Hebrides, where the house sparrow now breeds and the tree sparrow is absent.

Where house and tree sparrows have been introduced to the same country, the former has in all cases become dominant and the tree sparrow has not been very successful. Both species were brought to Australia about the same time but, whereas the house sparrow quickly asserted itself and has become common in inhabited places over a wide area, the tree sparrow has been confined to a rural habitat and is nowhere very common. This is especially interesting as the tree sparrows introduced to Australia came from China, where, as I have already mentioned, it is closely associated with man and behaves as a "house sparrow". The tree sparrow was brought to New Zealand in 1868, two years after the house sparrow, but it did not prosper and died out quite soon. In the United States, tree sparrows were introduced to St. Louis in 1870, before house sparrows were properly established there, and at first did well. Once the house sparrow began to spread the tree sparrows were forced out into the surrounding countryside, where they are to be found to-day, and have spread very little from the point of their original release. In Bermuda, where they were brought after the house sparrow was established, they failed to survive. On the other hand introductions to the East Indies (Celebes, Borneo and the Philippines), where, as far as I know, the house sparrow has not been introduced, have been very successful. Thus the house sparrow appears completely dominant: when it is already in occupation attempts to introduce tree sparrows have not been successful and in those places where it managed to establish itself in the house sparrow's absence the arrival of the latter has inhibited anything like a successful colonisation. Even in Ireland and Scotland, particularly in the islands of the latter, the house sparrow appears to have played some part in virtually eliminating the tree sparrow, though this is not the whole story: tree sparrows disappeared from the Isle of May in the Firth of Forth in 1922, three years before house sparrows began to breed there regularly and in several other places their numbers began to decrease before the house sparrows appeared.

The tree sparrow was first recorded in the Faroes in 1866 when it bred on Skuvoy; a pair bred at Torshavn in 1888 and birds were present on Kunoy at the beginning of the present century. It was believed to have become extinct by 1910, long before the arrival of the house sparrow; however there is a record of five birds on Mykines in the summer of 1935 and G. R. Potts found circumstantial evidence of breeding in Sunnbøur at the south of Suduroy in 1960—at least eleven tree sparrows including young birds were found occupying much the same area as a colony of house sparrows. Tree sparrows were not present in Sunnbøur in the summer of 1946, so it appears that the bird has re-colonised the Faroes since becoming extinct as a breeding species some forty years earlier. It will be most interesting to see if the two species continue to live side by side in Sunnbøur.* It is odd that Skuvoy, the island on which the most successful colony of tree sparrows was formed, should not yet have been occupied by house sparrows; the habitat is obviously a marginal one for both species and seems unlikely to support two closely-related sparrows in competition with each other.

It is difficult to account for the present situation in north-west Europe, though the following is suggested as a possible course of events: the tree sparrow reached northern Europe, including the north of the British Isles and the islands lying to the north and west, by spreading westwards from its original home in south-east Asia, before the house sparrow arrived by spreading from the south. The former species is much less strongly attached to man and would be expected to spread more rapidly across thinly populated areas. However, when the house sparrow arrived, the small species would be forced out from the inhabited areas, as happened in St. Louis, and is at present happening in Russian Turkestan, and would die out in those marginal areas that do not appear able to support two species of sparrows. Although the arrival of the house sparrow may have been the final factor in the elimination of the tree sparrow, it is clear that it was not the only one; for some other reason the bird was already losing ground in the extreme west before the house sparrow arrived and finished it off.

The house and tree sparrows have obviously been isolated geographically much longer than the house and Spanish sparrows and do not interbreed in nature, though in places they occupy the same habitat. Hybrids between house and tree sparrows have been bred in captivity and a number of wild hybrids between the two

* In 1961 Potts was unable to find tree sparrows on Sunnbøur.

species have been reported; though, without a definite record of
the nesting of a mixed pair, I feel that these reported hybrids are
open to a certain amount of doubt and could well refer to aberrantly
plumaged birds. It is difficult to visualise a free mating in the wild
between a male house sparrow and a female tree sparrow, which
to it would appear as a male, or between a male tree sparrow and a
female house sparrow, which to a tree sparrow would not appear
like its normal mate at all. Apart from the usual behavioural
barriers to mating between different species, mixed mating between
a sexually monomorphic and a dimorphic species appears improbable. P. Ruthke has reported a case of a hen tree sparrow sitting on
a clutch of five eggs with a cock house sparrow in attendance;
there were no other sparrows nearby and the assorted pair were
regularly seen at the nest. Unfortunately the clutch was deserted
so that it could not be established if this was a definite case of
hybridisation.

Two other sympatric species that are closely related to the
house sparrow are the scrub sparrow (*P. moabiticus*) and the Sind
jungle sparrow (*P. pyrrhonotus*). These are both birds of very
restricted distribution—the former in the Dead Sea Depression,
lower Tigris Valley and the mouth of the Karun River in
Afghanistan, the latter in the Indus Valley in West Pakistan
(Fig. 36: *11* and *13*, pp. 246 and 247). These two species are rather
similar to each other but are ecologically separated from the house
sparrow, breeding near water away from man, though they associate with the house sparrow out of the breeding season. Both were
probably established in their present areas before the arrival of the
house sparrow and indeed they may have had much wider distributions before the arrival of the latter confined them to their present
rather restricted habitats.

In this country the majority of house sparrows nest on buildings,
either in holes or in creepers growing on them. A small proportion
builds nests in trees and hedges, but still close to man's dwellings.
The nests, whether in the open or in a hole, are domed and are
entered through a small hole in the side. Thus the requirements of
a suitable nest-site for house sparrows are met by the nest built by
house martins, which also in this country most commonly nest on

man's buildings. Many of these nests, which remain over the winter, are occupied by sparrows when the martins are in their winter quarters and others are later usurped from the occupying martins. In America the cliff swallow and house finch suffer a similar persecution, while in Australia the same happens to the fairy martin. The house sparrow (and the tree sparrow) also makes use of the nests built by sand martins when they occupy sites near houses, but this is not very common and it is doubtful whether it can have any significant influence on the breeding of this species. At times both sparrows and martins have been recorded sharing the same hole. Swallows' nests are also used but the house sparrow seems less successful in defending these and a case of a returning pair of swallows evicting a brood of young sparrows has been reported.

As well as this appropriation of nests built by other species, the house sparrow competes for nesting sites with species that use holes, though only of course when these are near houses. House sparrows will displace tits from holes or nest-boxes; K. H. Hollick cites a case of sparrows ejecting young blue tits from a hole in the wall of a house. This hole was originally too small for the sparrows to enter, though they eventually did so by removing a loose piece of brick from the entrance. C. E. Martin observed a pair of house sparrows defending a nest-box against a pair of blue tits, although this also had a hole too small for the sparrows to enter and could be of no use to them. The sparrows eventually abandoned the nest-box and the tits were able to breed there. I have several times watched nuthatches in late March and early April clearing out the nesting material from a nest-box occupied by sparrows, though they never persisted in this. I never actually saw a fight between sparrows and nuthatches; the latter usually flew away when the sparrow appeared on the scene though whether the nuthatches deserted because of the sparrows or because they found the site unsuitable I am not able to say.

Competition over sites rarely occurs with starlings, which also nest in holes in buildings. The sparrows use entrance holes that are too small for starlings and avoid the holes suitable for the larger species, though sparrows sometimes roost in starling holes, follow-

ing the larger bird in after it has settled down. I have seen starlings
entering nest-boxes put up for sparrows and have watched the
sparrows attacking them. It is interesting that not only are the
starlings attacked by the pair owning the nest but also by other
sparrows that are near. Thus up to six birds may "buzz" the
starling, though it is usually only the owner male that will actually
strike it. In all cases I have observed, the starlings soon lost interest;
this was probably because the nest-boxes were not large enough for
them to breed in.

The swift on the other hand, does usurp both nest and nesting
material from house sparrows. Gilbert White suspected that this
was the case and recently A. S. Cutcliffe has shown that swifts will
expel house sparrows from their nests even when they have eggs.
Nest material was also stolen by swifts in spite of the house sparrows
being present at their nests; swifts may even take over sparrows'
nests and build their own on top of them; in a similar way I have
seen mistle thrushes stealing grass from a sparrow's nest in a tree
when the sparrows were present.

It is unlikely that this competition for nest-sites can have any
far reaching effect on species that do not mainly nest on buildings.
For example, the instance of a pair of sparrows evicting a family of
lesser spotted woodpeckers from a hole in a tree is more curious
than important. Again the number of sites where there is active
competition between swifts and sparrows is probably rather small
and is not likely to have a significant effect on the sparrow population. Sparrows, starlings and swifts all nested on my house in Hampshire but there was no competition between sparrows and the two
other species as they used holes too small for the larger birds to
enter; competition did occur, however, between swifts and starlings
which used the same entrance holes to the eaves.

On the other hand, the nest parasitism of house martins by
house sparrows and possibly also of cliff swallows and fairy martins
may have a limiting influence on the breeding success of these
species. It is not a recently acquired habit: Gilbert White in a letter
to Daines Barrington (26.2.1774) pointed out that the house
sparrow will dispossess both house and sand martins from their
nests. The house martin builds a solid nest, which, in its sheltered

position under the eaves of a house, may stay in place for several years and may be used by martins for a number of breeding seasons, and, as I have already pointed out, the resident house sparrow may thus take over a nest when the martins are in their winter quarters. House martins are a colonially nesting species; they have difficulty in evicting house sparrows from nests that have been appropriated and the presence of established pairs of house sparrows in the middle of a house martin colony when the martins return will probably have a disrupting effect on the breeding of the martins (though I should point out that I have watched house martins feeding young in a nest that touched another nest containing young house sparrows—the two species were paying no attention to each other). Later, when the martins return, disputes over nests occur, but in most cases they are unsuccessful in standing up to the sparrows. The house martin's nest is of intricate construction and the same nest is used for subsequent broods; thus its loss, together with the loss of the time spent in building, will effectively restrict the number of broods that can be raised by the martins. In both these ways the house sparrow may restrict the breeding success of the house martin.

Some observations were made over a period of years in southern England to find out the extent of appropriation of nests by sparrows before the return of the martins and also to find how frequently nests were usurped from martins after they had returned. Unfortunately it was not possible to continue the observations at any location for a period of years to find whether a colony could be maintained in the face of competition by sparrows, nevertheless circumstantial evidence was obtained that suggested that some breeding sites had been deserted, probably at least in part due to the influence of house sparrows. Observations were made on ninety-five old nests that had remained intact from the previous breeding season. Forty-four of these were occupied by sparrows before the return of the martins; thirty-seven were used again by martins and fourteen were not used. At the same colonies sixty new nests were built in the same period. The martins bred successfully in thirty-two of these; ten were appropriated by sparrows and eighteen were not used by either species for breeding. These results are summarised in Table 23. Several interesting points emerge from this: almost as many of the old nests were used by house sparrows as by house martins—the total of nests used by martins includes some that were incomplete and required patching up, which were thus not available for sparrows. House martins succeeded in breeding in only about fifty per cent of the new nests built. F. H. Lancum gives an instance of a farmhouse in Devon where out of eighteen new nests built, eleven (sixty-one per cent) were commandeered by house sparrows. Although sparrows actually bred in only seventeen per cent of the new nests, they were probably responsible for the martins failing to breed in many of the remaining nests because of interference. L. Rendall, for example, describes how sparrows not only dispossess martins of their nests, but also how they tear holes in newly built nests, remove the lining put in by the martins and also eject eggs and young.

TABLE 23

Usage of House Martins' Nests by Martins and Sparrows

	No. used by martins	No. used by sparrows	No. not used	Total
Old nests	37 (46%)	44 (39%)	14 (15%)	95
New nests	32 (53%)	10 (17%)	18 (30%)	60

The figure of seventeen per cent of new nests appropriated by sparrows is surprisingly high when it is considered that the house sparrow is a resident species, most members of which begin breeding at the end of April or early May before much nest building has been done by the martins. Some of the appropriation of new nests may be a result of sparrows losing their nests during the breeding season—R. M. Garnett describes how, when a sparrow's nest with an incomplete clutch was removed, the pair took over a martin's nest containing young; the adult martins as well as the young were forcibly ejected by the sparrows entering the nest and attacking the birds. Miss L. F. Anderson has described to me how, when an old martin's nest that had been taken over by sparrows fell down, the sparrows then appropriated a new nest that a pair of martins had almost completed. Most new nests are appropriated in May, presumably by first-year birds that have not up to then acquired a nest. In 1950 a pair of martins returned to an old nest which had partially collapsed and began patching it up on 4th May; the nest was almost complete by 12th May, when sparrows were seen in it for the first time. The martins were unsuccessful in evicting the sparrows, which reared two broods in the nest. On 18th May a martin was seen in the nest but flew off when a male sparrow arrived. Two martins again visited the nest on 15th June, when the sparrows had young, but made no attempt to enter. On the other hand, once the nest has been completed the entrance hole appears to be too small for the sparrow to enter and it is left alone.

L. R. Lewis has told me of some interesting observations he made at a house martin colony in 1953. This colony was on a school where there were normally about thirty nests, which were cleared away each autumn. On 15th March two male house sparrows were observed roosting on a ledge exactly where martins' nests had been built the previous summer, as shown by the tell-tale rings which remained. The sparrows were seen roosting in the same place on four occasions between 15th March and 9th April and during the day the roosting places were distinguishable by the droppings that had collected on the ledge. The site was not visited again until June when the martins had returned and built their nests. It was seen then that house sparrows had appropriated nests at just the two points where the birds had been observed roosting. House martins have bred for at least twenty years at this site and after their departure each autumn the nests have been removed. After the 1953 season at Mr. Lewis's suggestion the nests were not removed. Whereas in 1953 there were thirty-two nests with only two occupied by sparrows, there were only eleven nests in 1955 with at least six occupied by sparrows, four of these before the return of the martins. This is a remarkable decrease in the number of breeding pairs of martins and it would appear to be a result of the disruptive effect of sparrows in occupation in a house martin colony before the return of the martins. It also suggests that one method of preserving a house martin colony would be to remove their nests at the end of the breeding season so that a foothold is denied to the sparrows when the martins are away; this method was in fact used in Wisconsin in the United States at a cliff swallow colony, which as a result was able to build up in a remarkable way.

The martins are, however, not always unsuccessful. I have watched nests where martins have reared young in spite of attempts by sparrows to appropriate the nest. There have even been observations of martins imprisoning sparrows in nests they have usurped. F. C. R. Jourdain quotes an instance of how, after sparrows had taken possession of a nest, the martins built a further nest on top of the old one; after the martins had reared a brood the nest was removed and the remains of a sparrow was found in the old nest. A case has been reported from America where, after a male house sparrow had occupied a cliff swallow's nest and could not be evicted by the owners, a large party of swallows assembled at the nest and walled up the entrance. Months later, when the nest fell down, a mummified sparrow was found inside. It seems surprising that the sparrow is unable to peck its way out of the nest but it has been stated that sparrows cannot get into a martin's nest once the entrance has been completed and they always seize it before this stage is reached, suggesting that they are unable to break the structure. In a number of cases, I have observed martins breeding in nests after they have been used by sparrows, the martins first removing the lining of grass and straw that had been added. In general, however, there is little fighting and the house sparrow appears to be dominant. The martins prefer to attack the sparrows by flying at them and once they vacate the nest the sparrow moves in and is very difficult to dislodge. At this time of year the sparrow spends prolonged periods in or beside the nest and the martins get little opportunity of re-occupying it.

It would be interesting to know what happens to the pair of martins that is dispossessed. Certainly in some colonies that I watched the pairs did not build a further nest; either they must have failed to breed that season or else have moved away some distance. On the other hand when nests have been removed by man the birds will frequently re-build in the same place, provided that it is not too late in the season. We know little of the structure of a house martin colony; it may be that the adults prefer to return to the old nests and that new nests are usually built by first-year birds. If this is the case it would suggest that the occupation of old nests by sparrows might have a more disruptive influence than the actual figures of appropriated old nests suggest by themselves.

At no colony were observations made for a sufficiently long time to follow the effect of continued nest-site parasitism. However, at one site where there were ten old nests, all of these were occupied by sparrows before the martin's return. The martins visited the nests in May for some days but did not recover any. This colony had obviously been displaced and it is interesting that the same year a new colony of thirteen nests was established a short distance away on some new houses that had only been completed since the last breeding season; only one of these nests was usurped by sparrows. In another group of houses there were two nests in 1949 and four nests in 1950. From the number of "rings" visible under the eaves this colony had clearly been much larger in previous years. One of the nests in 1950 was usurped by sparrows and another fell down, probably after interference by sparrows. Some martins returned in 1951 but no nests were built in that year or the two following. In three other colonies that were under observation the number of breeding pairs decreased successively from 1951 to 1953.

A more striking example of the influence of house sparrows on house martins has been given by C. Russell. At his farm, the house martins, formerly numerous, became fewer and fewer until in 1869 young flew from only about two nests. In 1870 Russell began to kill the sparrows and the martins so recovered that by 1884 there were one hundred and seventy nests and in 1885 over two hundred. He cites another example where, after sparrows had occupied all the martins' nests on a house, they were systematically shot; in two years there were twenty martins' nests but the shooting was discontinued and the sparrows again moved in and no more young martins were reared. I. O. Buss gives a similar example from America where a cliff swallow colony built up from one nest to two thousand in thirty-eight years when the house sparrows, which had been usurping the nests, were systematically destroyed; this is the case where, as already mentioned, the nests were removed after the breeding season so that the sparrows could not move in when the owners were away. In a study of another American species, the house finch, W. H. Bergtold found that, in spite of determined efforts on his part, sixteen per cent of the eggs were destroyed by house sparrows; further he points out that this figure does not include the large potential loss brought about by the destruction of house finches' nests by sparrows before eggs had been laid in them.

There is no doubt that the house martin has decreased markedly in numbers over the past fifty to a hundred years in this country. The main reason that has been advanced is the diminution of its food supplies caused by increased industrialisation and improved sanitation that no doubt has decreased the number of insects. This has meant that the house martin is now largely restricted to the smaller towns and villages. (Little information is available on the cliff nesting colonies of house martins, though E. M. Nicholson considers them to be substantial.) It does not appear likely that nest-site parasitism by house sparrows could by itself have been responsible for this decrease—presumably house sparrows were well entrenched in man's houses before house martins left cliff sites for houses, which itself must have occurred some long time ago; obviously such suitable sites would quickly have been adopted by house sparrows and yet the decrease in martins is comparatively recent—but together with other factors it may well have had a contributory effect. Observations at some house sparrow colonies have suggested that there may be a shortage of suitable sites for nests. This has probably become more acute with the change from thatched to slate-roofed houses and thus the appropriation of house martins' nests may have increased in the last hundred years. In Ireland the house martin is much commoner than in Britain; E. M. Nicholson has associated this with the much higher incidence of flies but it is possibly not without relevance that the house sparrow is much less widely distributed in Ireland than in Great Britain. A recent report gives details of house martins laying their eggs on a narrow ledge instead of the normal enclosed cup; presumably this is done by pairs that have been dispossessed and have not had time to build another nest and though obviously not purposeful could evolve as a way of defeating the interference by house sparrows.

The house sparrow suffers little in their way from other birds. It is only rarely parasitised by the cuckoo. A. W. Boyd quotes a record for the last century and C. S. S. Ellison saw a young cuckoo being fed by a house sparrow in 1928. In Lancashire in 1908, H. Massey found a cuckoo's egg in a nest in a tree together with four sparrow's eggs and the following year another egg was found in a sparrow's nest at the same place in a roof of a building; this particular cuckoo was known to lay normally in meadow pipits' nests, which were scarce locally in 1908 and 1909.

M. Rothschild and T. Clay have suggested that the impulse of birds to usurp the nests of other species may be one way in which brood parasitism has originated. This adds interest to a remarkable observation made by D. Stonor at a cliff swallow colony; there were about fifty nests in this colony, two of which were used by house sparrows. A third nest contained three swallows' eggs and one house sparrow's egg. These were incubated by the swallows and the sparrow hatched first. Although two of the swallows' eggs subsequently hatched, the young did not survive. The young sparrow was fed by the swallows alone and was still alive fourteen days after hatching, when it weighed twenty-three grammes and was almost ready to fly. Its further progress was unfortunately not recorded. I. O. Buss gives other records of sparrows' eggs being hatched out by cliff swallows but he does not mention if the birds were reared to fledging. There is also a record of young house sparrows being brooded by a swift, though it is not clear if this was a case of brood parasitism.

It seems appropriate in this chapter to mention a number of other interactions between house sparrows and various animals, though these have probably little ecological significance. Nevertheless they help to give us some insight into the general behaviour of the bird. A number of writers have commented on the house sparrow's habit of chasing larger birds, particularly pigeons and starlings; other species that I have seen chased include rook, crow and mistle thrush. In the case of the pigeon, the sparrow at times seems to be attempting to pluck out feathers for its nest; the other birds are potential enemies, either as competitors for nest and roosting holes, robbers of nesting material or predators. There are other cases, however, in which it seems that it is merely the sight of the larger bird flying away that is enough to stimulate a following reaction. When the larger bird lands the sparrow normally lands beside it; the attack is not pressed home and the sparrow shows its nervousness by flicking its tail.

House sparrows regularly follow cats, keeping in cover and above ground level. With small mammals such as mice, voles and rats the sparrow will descend to the ground and follow closely behind. An instance has been described of eight sparrows escorting a lame rat across a road; the birds dispersed themselves round the rat about two to three feet away, chirping excitedly until the procession disappeared out of sight. Similar behaviour has been reported with a vole; in this case the animal was uninjured and made rushes at the sparrows but, although they flew up out of the way, they regularly came back. On other occasions when a weasel or a rat has been seen to rush at a sparrow, the bird merely rose a foot or so in the air and landed again in the same place, apparently unconcerned. The main significance of this behaviour appears to be that a possible predator is kept in view; in a social species, this may be advantageous in warning other individuals of a possible danger.

CHAPTER 17

HOUSE SPARROWS AND MAN

THE LIFE of the house sparrow is intimately bound up with that of man and it is perhaps interesting to discuss this relationship separately from both points of view: that of the sparrow and that of man.

In previous chapters we have seen how the species evolved in close association with agricultural man; this evolution has continued and in many places the bird has emancipated itself from the agricultural background and is now largely associated with urbanised man. For example, it is interesting to note that E. Coues, writing about the house sparrow in America in 1879, stated that: "here they still live for the most part, in cities, towns and villages, where they derive their subsistence chiefly from street-garbage, especially horse-manure"; W. B. Barrows, when discussing the spread of the house sparrow in North America, remarked that any birds that were introduced to farms near towns did not stay but moved to the town. In the United States the bird spread from town to town along railway lines in box cars and so on and it was not until the towns were fully occupied that a movement took place into suburban and rural areas, especially in grain-growing districts. In the early days of the colonisation, farms that were visited by flocks of birds in the autumn to feed on the ripening grain were deserted by the sparrows at other times of the year.

One of the main features of the sparrow's habitat to-day is the presence of buildings, preferably occupied ones; for the house sparrow will normally only nest in unoccupied buildings if they are close to inhabited ones. In an optimum sparrow habitat the buildings are close together, though there must also be patches of open ground, as occurs in suburbs and cities like London, where there are numbers of parks and squares among the houses. This meets the requirements of a regular supply of food provided by the human inhabitants, together with ground that supplies a certain amount of vegetable food for the adults and insect food for the young. The bird, however, occurs even in towns where the open spaces are very restricted, as a walk through the streets before the traffic is moving will show, and they are also to be found in such barren habitats as factory sites and railway stations:

> . . . underneath the station's high arched dome
> A dozen happy sparrows make their home!
> Perhaps they like the bustle and the din,
> The sooty railway air to flutter in—
>   The shining rails, the steam, the distant drums,
>   The picking of the rail-bars scattered crumbs,
> And engine smoke ascending, dense and blue,
> The clatter as the Royal Scot comes through!
>   *Joan Pomfret*

Many of these latter birds appear to spend much of their lives completely under cover. There is an even more extraordinary newspaper report of sparrows nesting in a coal mine in Northumberland in 1956 hundreds of feet below the ground, where they were being fed by the miners; unfortunately I was unable to confirm this, but it does suggest a most interesting development.

The optimum habitat requirements are also met in highly populous arable land, particularly where this is associated with chicken and pig farming, which provides an additional supply of food throughout the year. In less highly populated farming areas, even when there is considerable cereal production, the sparrow population is much less dense, presumably because these areas do not provide the same level of food at all seasons of the year. The house sparrow is so sedentary in its behaviour that only where buildings and open farming areas are side by side does the population density reach its maximum. House sparrow habitats thus tend to be isolated from each other, though in the summer months with the ripening of weed seeds and grain they tend to expand and may become contiguous over large areas, thus allowing interchange of young birds between neighbouring colonies. House sparrows appear reluctant to move over habitats unsuitable to them and, without this seasonal change, spread to new areas would be much reduced and highly-inbred populations would be formed.

Although we normally associate the house sparrow with an urban habitat, it is able to tolerate conditions far removed from this, provided man is present. G. Mountfort reported that sparrows were present at the camps in the rear of the 8th Army in the North African desert during the Second World War and also at a U.S. Army Depot in the Mojave Desert, one of the hottest places in the U.S.A. In some places even the presence of man does not appear to be necessary. In the high country of the Hindu Kush, the Pamirs, the Karakoram range and the western Himalayas the "house sparrow" is the tree sparrow, a resident species completely occupying the house sparrow niche. Whereas, as we have seen, the house sparrow is a summer visitor only and, what is more, tends to breed in holes in cliffs and earth banks rather than in houses. These house sparrows (sub-sp. *parkini*) winter in the northern plains of India and Pakistan and it is interesting that in their winter quarters C. B. Ticehurst found them right out in the grass jungle away from habitations where they did not associate with the resident birds (sub-sp. *indicus*). In addition, even when the house sparrow is a resident, there are a number of isolated instances of its breeding away from man. In most of these the birds are reported as breeding in cliffs, but there is a recent account by J. N. Hobbs of breeding colonies in trees and bushes in open grazing country in the Riverina district of New South Wales; some of these colonies were up to twenty miles from the nearest human habitations, most seemed to be associated with water and particularly with the introduced African Boxthorn (*Pyracathus*), which supplied nest-sites. These birds presumably subsist largely on grass seeds.

In an interesting paper by G. R. Williams on the dispersal of introduced European species from the mainland of New Zealand to the surrounding islands, instances are given of house sparrows breeding on some of the unoccupied islands (see Fig. 31, p. 184). Williams is of the opinion that the birds are not able to sustain a breeding colony in the absence of human inhabitants and that where breeding continues the breeding stock must be made up by periodic arrivals from the mainland. However, K. Wodzicki believes that a successful colony has established itself on White Island, thirty-two miles off the coast of the North Island of New

Zealand in the Bay of Plenty, after this island was evacuated by man; these birds were breeding in cliff sites in 1947 and 1949, though none were present in 1925. A colony of house sparrows also breeds on Goose Island, lying in the Bass Strait between Tasmania and the mainland of Australia. No one has lived on this island for many years, the nearest habitations being on Flinders and Cape Barren Islands, respectively fifteen and ten miles away; like the Australian birds seen by Hobbs, these sparrows breed in boxthorn bushes.

In several desert regions there is evidence of breeding away from man. In Cyrenaica, J. K. Stanford informs me that he found a colony in *zizyphus* bushes at a water hole ten miles away from the nearest habitation; he suggests that these birds could possibly have fed on the corn sowed there by the Bedouin and left to ripen—there were also a good deal of insect life and grass seeds near the water. In the Escalante Desert in Utah, C. Cottam suggested that the introduced house sparrow was breeding twenty miles from the nearest houses. H. St. J. B. Philby mentions a colony in central Arabia far away from houses and R. Meinertzhagen says that in Arabia the house sparrow is a bird of acacia and other trees, not of dwellings, and is found in colonies hundreds of miles from buildings and farmland. In Palestine it is also said to nest in caves and holes in cliffs far from human houses and villages.

There are other examples from different parts of the bird's range where it is apparently not strictly dependent on man, though the evidence is less clear-cut than that given above. This behaviour must nonetheless be regarded as exceptional and in many cases evacuation of an area by man has led to the disappearance of the sparrow. Nevertheless it does provide further proof of the adaptability of the species. Presumably in these places the conditions are suitable for maintaining a supply of food throughout the year and competition by other small seed-eating birds is absent. Even in this country and in other parts of Europe pairs will at times breed some distance away from occupied buildings; usually, however, these are isolated instances and no breeding colony is built up.

The bird's tolerance of climatic conditions is also remarkable: it is resident at Kiruna in Sweden, where winter temperatures may

PLATE 21. Sparrows on car radiator: the birds use their tails for support on the smooth surface. (*E. Hosking*)

PLATE 22. House sparrows feeding from man's hand in London Park

fall below —15°F.; at Cuiba, the capital of the State of Mato Grosso, in central Brazil, where the mean temperature ranges from 75°F. in the winter to 81°F. in the summer with midday temperatures above 100°F.; and in Sind, where summer temperatures regularly reach 110–120°F. It appears equally at home in Aden where the average annual rainfall is three inches and in Burma where it exceeds one hundred inches.

How then does this bird that is so closely associated with man view his universal provider? The house sparrow could never be described as tame; familiar yes (Plate 21, p. 212), but also extremely wary. It is, of course, quite possible to obtain tame house sparrows by rearing them from a few days old, but it is interesting that, unlike the related weavers, they do not readily accept captivity and rarely breed in confinement. I have managed to get hand-reared birds to breed in an aviary, but only when I supplied maggots in addition to bread, seeds and greenstuff, and even then the breeding success was very low. This wariness may, however, be one of the keys to the sparrow's success, natural selection having eliminated the less wary individuals. This would of course be of less importance to species like robin and chaffinch, where most individuals do not come closely into contact with man. Even in the comprehensive Bird Protection Act of 1954, the house sparrow is still outlawed and in the German Nature Conservation Order of 1936 the house sparrow was included among the unprotected birds; in many other countries also it is a proscribed species. Hence the premium on wariness remains. Yet with a little effort sparrows can be tamed as a visit to the London parks will show; here they can be seen taking food from the hands and perching on individuals who have won their confidence (Plate 22, p. 213). W. H. Hudson remarked on this in his *Birds in London* and it can still be seen to-day; again this provides further evidence of adaptability—behaviour modified to suit the situation. Their impudence is also well-known: they enter hospital wards through open windows to steal scraps from the floors, and in open-air cafés they will land on the tables and take crumbs from the plates. The tree sparrow (*P. montanus*), in the east where it behaves as a "house sparrow", is, if anything, more cheeky, regularly coming inside houses and even nesting in occupied rooms; in India the house sparrow too is a frequent visitor to the open shops and houses.

The house sparrow's wariness is also shown by its attitude towards traps; although the juveniles are easily caught in all types of trap, the adults, unlike other garden birds, are very reluctant to enter except when their customary caution is overcome by the urgency of collecting food for a nestful of young. When I began my study of sparrows, I attempted to trap my local flock by means of a simple hand-operated drop trap. This was successful for one or two week-ends, but after this the house sparrows refused to enter, though they perched on a nearby apple tree, flew down at the blue tits that were taking bread out of the trap and, rather like miniature skuas, forced the tits to drop the bread. As I have already mentioned in an earlier chapter, sparrows once trapped are rarely caught a second time. J. P. Porter carried out some simple experiments on house sparrows that illustrate well their cautious attitude. Food was put out in an open space over a period of sixteen days and records kept of the distance from the food at which the birds alighted. On the first day the average was forty-six inches; on the fifth day this had decreased to about twenty inches but for the rest of the time there was no further reduction—not a single bird actually alighted beside the food.

CHAPTER 18

MAN AND THE HOUSE SPARROW

MAN'S ATTITUDES towards the house sparrow can be classed under three heads: sentimental, scientific and economic. Sparrows have never occupied a place like that of the robin in Britain nor have they caught the attention of poets like the nightingale and lark; yet to many people they must be the most familiar of all wild animals and their bustle and chatter brings life to the centres of cities and other man-made sterile places. Scientifically the bird has been much neglected; this is somewhat counterbalanced by the enormous amount that has been written on its destructiveness and damage to man's interests, though much of this is ill-founded and biased from one point of view or another.

The sparrow is mentioned many times in the Bible, but the name may often be used as a generic term for a small bird and need not necessarily refer to the house sparrow, though Alexander the Myndian in the 1st Century A.D. distinguished between house and tree sparrows. Even to-day in many Middle Eastern languages there are no words to distinguish the different species of small birds. Three pet sparrows grace the pages of literature. Catullus (b. 84 B.C.) wrote two poems about a pet sparrow belonging to his lover Lesbia, as he called the wife of the consul, Q. Metellus Celer. There is some doubt if the subject of these poems was in fact a house sparrow, or for that matter a sparrow at all, but there is no doubt that this bird was intended in John Skelton's *Book of Philip Sparrow*. Philip was evidently a common name for sparrows and clearly identifies the species—"All sparrows are called Philip; 'Phip Phip' they cry." Skelton's poem was written at the beginning of the sixteenth century, supposedly inspired by the death of Jane Scrope's pet sparrow—

> That cat specially
> That slew so cruelly
> My litell pretty sparowe
> That I brought up at Carowe.

but obviously both poets were moved more by the attractions of the owners than those of their pets.

Mrs. Clare Kipps's sparrow Clarence is without doubt the most widely known. Her book *Sold for a Farthing* has been published in many languages and has been read all over the world. This is the fascinating story of a bird reared from a few days old and living on terms of great intimacy with his mistress for many years; while sentiment is rightly there, this book is also a valuable scientific contribution to the study of animal behaviour. John Clare in his Diary describes another pet sparrow that lived in his house and even became friendly with the family cat; so much so that the latter allowed the bird to perch on its back and take pieces of bread from between its paws. Another sparrow that achieved immortality for rather different reasons is the one already mentioned as being killed at Lord's by a ball bowled by Jehangir Khan in the match between the M.C.C. and Cambridge University on 3rd July, 1936. This bird has been preserved and can now be seen mounted on the ball in the Memorial Gallery at Lord's (Plate 23a, p. 220).

The house sparrow can readily be obtained and kept in cages without evoking much sentimental opposition and for this reason has been used fairly frequently, particularly in the U.S.A., as a laboratory animal. Much of the work on the metabolism of birds carried out by Dr. S. C. Kendeigh and his co-workers at the University of Illinois made use of sparrows, numerous workers have used sparrows in photostimulation experiments and it has featured extensively in work on endocrinology. It has also some claim to fame in that it was used in the early French high altitude balloon tests and was one of the bird species used for the first demonstration of the transmission of the malarial parasite (*Plasmodium*) in India. It is not, however, a popular aviary species as it does not, in general, settle down well and only very rarely has been bred successfully in captivity.

The economic ornithology of the sparrow dates back at least to New Testament times: "Are not two sparrows* sold for a farthing?" In Tudor times, as shown by an entry in the Hunstanton

---

* Not necessarily house sparrows, though no doubt these were included.

Household Book, 1519–78—"How xij sparrows of gyste"—
sparrows were contributed in lieu of rent. These birds were
probably trapped, probably for their destruction rather than for
food, but by the middle of the sixteenth century the practice of
hanging unglazed earthenware pots under the eaves of houses so
that sparrows would nest in them and the fledgelings could be
removed and eaten had been adopted (Plate 23b, p. 220). This
appears to have originated in the Low Countries and was probably
introduced to Britain at the beginning of the seventeenth century
by Dutch engineers who came over to drain the Fens. The practice
was continued until the middle of the last century, though possibly
as much to protect the thatched roofs as to collect the young for the
pot. On the Continent it certainly persisted into this century—
Collingwood Ingram mentions them in the Vosges during the
First World War—and may still continue in some parts to this day;
for instance, C. B. Ticehurst remarked on them in Malta in 1911.
Dr. C. de Lucca informs me that glazed earthenware gin bottles
with the bottoms knocked off are still hung up in Malta for sparrows to nest in, though the practice is now dying out as bottles
of this type are no longer imported and the existing ones are disappearing through breakage. Sparrow pie was a regular country
dish until the First World War—"the sparrow is excellent food,
and a great restorer of decayed nature"—but, with improvement
in the standard of living and the disappearance of cheap domestic
labour necessary for preparing enough sparrows to make an adequate meal, it has disappeared from the menu. At one time both
sparrows and their eggs were taken as an aphrodisiac; doubtless an
analogy with the bird's own behaviour rather than for any other
reason—as Linnaeus says in his description of the bird "*Sala-
cissimus qui vigesies saepe coit.*"

During the eighteenth and nineteenth centuries house sparrows
were also being killed because of their injuries to man's interests.
Most parishes had "Sparrow Clubs", formed with the objective of
destroying as many sparrows as possible, or paid out "sparrow
money" from the accounts for both dead birds and eggs. It is
interesting to look at some of the rates paid. Records go back to
1744 in Warwickshire, where in 1768 the price paid was twopence

per dozen; in Suffolk at this time it was threepence. In Scarborough in 1809 threepence per dozen was being paid for birds and one penny per dozen for eggs. In Worsborough in 1820 the price had risen to sixpence. Threepence per dozen appears to have been the standard rate throughout the country for the next fifty years, though as much as tenpence half-penny was being paid in Guernsey—there is an entry for £72 5s. 8d. for Sparrow Money in Guernsey in 1827; this represents about twenty thousand birds, a considerable total for one year. Sparrow Money ceases to appear in parish accounts about 1870; one of the latest records shows cocks at one shilling and hens still at sixpence per dozen. The reason for this differentiation between the sexes is not clear, though the lower rates for nestlings, three halfpence to threepence, and eggs, one penny to three halfpence, shows an appreciation of hatching and fledging success. The Wirral Farmers' Club that offered sixpence per dozen in 1884 for birds taken up to the end of March had definitely begun to put the practice on a more sound scientific basis. Some clubs have persisted to the present day as a recent report in the *Manchester Guardian* of the annual general meeting of the Elham Sparrow Club in Kent shows.

It is not easy to guess what effect this had on the sparrow population. Most of the records suggest that the numbers destroyed in a parish were quite small, one or two thousand or less per year, but J. Cordeaux writing on the birds of the Humber district in 1872 noted an increase in the numbers of house sparrows and attributed this to the discontinuance of the time-honoured custom of paying Sparrow Money.

Against this background of the house sparrow being considered as a pest in Britain its widespread introduction to America and other parts of the world becomes even more surprising. It did not take long, however, for the attitude to the house sparrow to change in these countries. New Zealand doubtless welcomed its first birds in 1866, but in twenty years' time Sparrow Clubs on the, by now almost extinct, English pattern were being formed and offering payment for heads and eggs. The climate of opinion began to turn against the sparrow in the U.S.A. about 1880, though even at that time, and for the next few years, birds continued to be transported from the east to states in the centre and south where the bird had not yet penetrated—a Canadian is reported to have said: "What wonder that the English farmer stared in blank amazement when he first heard of it (the introduction of sparrows to the U.S.), or that he failed to account for its action, except on the assumption that America had been visited by a wave of temporary insanity." Up to this time the bird was protected in most states, but these protection laws began to be repealed and offensive measures against sparrows introduced in their place: for example, in 1883 the following law in Pennsylvania: "Be it enacted that from and after the passage of this act it shall be lawful at any season of the year to kill or in any way destroy the small bird known as the English Sparrow." By 1889 W. B. Barrows could record seven states in the area of the original introductions that had laws aimed against sparrows; two of these states were at that time offering bounties of about ten cents per dozen for dead sparrows. These bounties did not continue to be paid for long; either the inducement was not great enough to attract people to kill them or substantial sums were being paid out for a crop of sparrows that would have probably died from other density-dependent effects without making a significant reduction in the annual breeding population. When the bird was first introduced to Bermuda fines were imposed on anyone killing it, but in ten years the law was altered and bounties were being offered for its destruction; nearly three hundred dollars were expended to this end in the next two years but the payment was discontinued as it was having no appreciable effect on the population.

The same attitude now holds in other places that have had deliberate introductions and came in time, as we have seen, to prevent the ingress of sparrows to Western Australia. A diatribe that appeared in the *Adelaide Garden and Field* in 1887 shows how opinions had changed in Australia in twenty-five years:

> What means this sadly plaintive wail,
> Ye men of spades and ploughs and harrows?
> Why are your faces wan and pale?
> It is the everlasting sparrows.

We may demolish other pests
That devastate the farm and garden;
But spoiled by these voracious guests,
Our prospects are not worth a farden.

We can't defeat a foe like this
With gunshot or with bows and arrows;
We must resort to artifice
To cope with enemies like sparrows.

Our level best we all have tried
With scarecrows, nets, and cunning cages,
Our utmost efforts they deride,
And spoil our fruit in all its stages.

Lift up your heads, your hearts lift up,
Resume your spades, your ploughs and harrows.
And while you drain the genial cup,
I'll tell you how to lick the sparrows.

No more your wasted fruits bewail,
Your crops destroyed of peas and marrows,
A cure there is that cannot fail
To rid you of the hateful sparrows.

The remedy is at your feet,
Slay them and wheel them out in barrows,
Poisoned by Faulding's Phoenix wheat,
The one great antidote to sparrows.
                    Adelaide Post Laureate

Whether this was followed by a campaign against the sparrows
I have not been able to find out but if it was the evidence is that it
was not very successful. The house sparrow is still numerous to-day
in Australia and remains the bane of the farmer, horticulturist and
gardener, as it does in many other parts of the world.

Some effort must be made to consider dispassionately how far
this viewpoint is justified. The difficulty in considering the case
of the sparrow lies not least in its catholic feeding habits, its
adaptability to local conditions and its ability to exploit new
sources of food as they occur. The house sparrow as we have seen
in Chapter 4 is basically a seed-eater, though the nestlings eat a

THIS SPARROW WAS KILLED AT LORD'S BY A BALL
BOWLED BY JEHANGIR KHAN (CAMBRIDGE UNIVERSITY)
TO T.N.PEARCE (M.C.C.)
ON JULY 3RD 1936

PLATE 23. *Above*: Young house sparrow and the cause of its death. (*Wallace Heaton Ltd*). *Below*: Sparrow-pot; the pot is placed against a wall so that the larger hole is closed. (*C. Ingram*)

PLATE 24. Male house sparrow and blue tit. The house sparrow is dominant over many of the other small garden species and drives them away from food. (*E. Hosking*)

considerable amount of animal food (see Chapter 8) and in its association with man the bird has become almost omnivorous. Quantitative information on the different types of food taken is thus necessary if we are to attempt to make some assessment of the bird's importance to man; this has been provided to some extent by crop and stomach analyses that have been made in many different parts of the house sparrow's range. It must, however, be appreciated that these studies have for obvious reasons been carried out in agricultural areas, whereas as I have pointed out earlier the house sparrow is now as much an inhabitant of towns as a parasite of agriculture—the movements of house sparrows, even the movement to the ripening grain fields, are so limited that the populations must be divided into two groups: those living in towns and suburbs, which probably do not come into contact with agriculture, and those living on the outskirts of towns, in villages and around farms, where they are in range of cereal crops. The bias of the results is illustrated by the fact that E. R. Kalmbach in his analysis of the stomach contents of 4,848 adults included bread among "other vegetable matter", which amounted to only about 0·5 per cent.

H. N. Southern has reviewed the work on stomach analyses and Table 24, which is taken from his paper with, in addition, some more recent results by Frk. M. Hammer in Denmark, summarises the information. It will be seen that taken on a yearly basis, vegetable matter makes up for about eighty-five to ninety-five per cent of the food eaten by birds living in arable districts and that in the majority of these seventy-five to eighty per cent was made up of cereals. These birds were able to obtain grain not only as it ripened in the fields or was stooked but throughout the year from granaries and feed to chickens and other domestic animals; some of this must have been spillage or gleanings from the fields, but clearly most of it must be regarded as loss. Kalmbach in America was able to separate the cereals taken into "feed", including waste, and grain taken from the fields; it is interesting that even during the harvest the latter only amounted to forty per cent and over the whole year less than twenty per cent. It has been estimated that a single sparrow consumes from six to eight pounds of food per year so that in an agricultural area it can be seen that a high sparrow

TABLE 24: Summary of stomach content examinations of the house

Name	Date	No. of specimens examined	Method	Food in: Spring	Summer
J. M. Gurney, C. Russell and E. Coues	1885	694	Occurrence %	Corn Greens Seeds Seed corn Insects	Corn Greens Seeds Insects
W. E. Collinge	1912–27	758	Volumetric	—	—
			do.	—	—
		476	do.	—	—
L. Florence	1912–15	146	Occurrence %	Corn Insects	Corn Weeds Insects
W. B. Barrows	1889	522	do.	—	Cereals 42% Veg. 20% Weeds 19% Insects 13% Fruit 6%
E. R. Kalmbach	1940	4848	Volumetric	Feed Cereals Insects Weeds	Feed Cereals Weeds Insects
		2819	do.	—	—
T. Arinkina and I. Kolesnikov	1927	990	Occurrence %	—	—
	1927	1231	do.	—	—
K. I. Rusinova	1926	1321	do.	Weeds	Weeds Corn
Schleh	1883–4	263	do.	Insects Weeds Corn	Corn Weeds Insects
M. Hammer	1941–3	2657	do.	Grain Insects Weeds	Weeds Insects Grain

* Items are given in order of importance.

sparrow (after H. N. Southern)*

Food in: Autumn	Winter	Proportions for year %		Nestling %		Conditions
Corn Seeds	Corn Seeds	Corn Seeds Insects	75 10 4	Corn Insects (Lepid. larv. Coleopt.	40 50 40 10	England, arable
—	—	Cereals Seeds Insects	75 10 5	—		England, arable
—	—	Insects Seeds Cereals Buds	35 20 17 9	—		England, fruit-growing district
—	—	—		Inj. insects Mixed veg. (total anim.	88 4·5 95·5)	England: 200 from fruit-growing district, 122 from suburban district
Corn Weeds	Corn Weeds	Corn Weeds Insects	81 15·5 3·5	—		Scotland N.E., arable
—	—	—		—		U.S.A., urban and park area, Washington, D.C.
Feed Weeds Cereals	Feed Weeds Cereals	Feed Cereals Weeds Insects	60 18 17 4	—		U.S.A., all parts
—	—	—		Insects Feed	68 30	do.
—	—	Corn Weeds Insects	50** 46** 4	—		U.S.S.R., Turkestan
—	—	—		Insects Corn Insects	70 19 77·8	do.
—	—	Weeds Corn Insects	83** 12·5** 3**	—		
orn eeds sects	—	Insects Weeds Corn	35 34 31	Insects Corn	50 50	Germany, garden on edge of town
eeds ain sects	Grain Weeds Insects	Cereals Weeds Insects	45 42 13	Insects Grain Weeds	79 19 2	Denmark, Agricultural Research Stations

** May–August.

population could cause a considerable amount of loss. In addition to the grain actually eaten, a further loss is caused in the fields close to towns and villages by the birds perching on the stalks and shaking the grain from the ripening heads; in the fields that are visited a band about five yards deep can be almost cleared of grain and where large flocks form, this band gets beaten down in a characteristic way. When the crop is stooked, much of the exposed grain can be quickly removed by a flock of sparrows.

The amount of damage decreases rapidly with the distance of the grain field from the nearest breeding area and K. Mansfeld reckoned that no damage occurred in fields above two miles away. My own observations and those of others confirm that the grain-field flocks are not drawn from greater distances than this; hence it is probable that significant damage is only caused within an area a mile or so distant from the edge of a village or town—in highly-populated districts this could of course account for a considerable proportion of the total crop being lost. Where the bird is a summer visitor, the restriction in numbers caused by the necessity for an adequate supply of food to be available throughout the year is not so pressing, provided sufficient food can be obtained in the winter quarters. In parts of Turkestan, for example, D. N. Kashkarov has estimated that about thirty per cent of the wheat grown is destroyed by sparrows (including tree and Spanish as well as house sparrows). This rate of damage is probably rather exceptional but there is no doubt that significant damage to crops is caused in many parts of the bird's range, even allowing for the fact that much of the grain taken is gleaned from the ground and is waste already lost to man. In the results from Turkestan the proportion of cereal is much lower, the balance being made up by weed seeds, an indication that here the agricultural methods are less efficient. The figures from a fruit-growing district in England and from a suburban area in Germany show much lower proportions of cereals (seventeen per cent and thirty-one per cent respectively) and even from the agricultural research stations in Denmark the total was still less than half. No results are available from urban areas where the amount of grain accessible to the sparrows, more particularly since the disappearance of the horse from the centres of cities, must be small; the bulk of the diet of these birds must surely be bread and other scraps, much of it put out deliberately for the birds, together with some weed seeds. Even in arable areas it is likely that the amount of grain available to sparrows has decreased since these analyses were made; this is partly a result of increased mechanisation of farming, which means that the ripe grain is in the fields for a shorter time, and also the trend towards battery hens and broiler production, which keeps hens and their food indoors and away from sparrows. This must either force a change in feeding habits or result in a reduction in numbers.

Although less grain is taken in suburban and fruit-growing districts, sparrows may still cause damage by eating buds and nipping the leaves off seedling vegetables; the incidence of these attacks seems to be rather local and sporadic and they are generally more of a nuisance than of economic importance.

Another charge that the farmer levels against sparrows is that they may assist the spread of various poultry diseases by being hosts for the poultry red mite and the hen flea, both of which are known disease vectors. While sparrows certainly live in close association with hens, no evidence is available that they are of real importance as agents in the transmission of disease.

Sparrows regularly spend much time in factory buildings and stores and the droppings from these birds, particularly when they roost inside the buildings, may cause a considerable amount of damage apart from making the place rather unpleasant for the work people. The birds are encouraged to come into these places by scraps of food that are left around, or even deliberate feeding, particularly where large doors or windows are left open and provide the birds with easy access, as well as by the security they offer for roosting. At one period in America roosting sparrows also caused much damage to creepers, trees and the footpaths beneath them, but this was when the bird became extraordinarily common there; now that the population density has fallen to a figure comparable with that in other parts, it seems to be less remarked. In Britain the starling causes more damage and annoyance from its roosting habits than does the sparrow. Again in buildings the bulky nests of dried grass may increase fire risks and Kalmbach states that insurance companies in the United States take note of this when assessing premiums for warehouses and similar buildings, and indeed a recent newspaper report suggests a sparrow that carried a burning cigarette end to its nest in Suffolk was directly responsible for setting a cottage on fire. It is said that sparrows with lighted straws attached to their tails were used to destroy the Romano-British town of Galleva Atrebatum.

Another interference with man's activities was caused by the sparrow that was sucked into the engine of a 40-ton K.L.M. Viscount at Manchester Airport on 28th April, 1958 and resulted in the aircraft being grounded for over six hours. This we can hardly hold specifically against the sparrow, aerodrome haunting species like the skylark and lapwing being more likely to cause this sort of trouble.

The final charge that has been put against the sparrow, particularly in those areas to which it has been recently introduced and has become abundant, is that it is responsible for driving away more beneficial birds that would otherwise be present. There seems no doubt that the growth of a population of several million house sparrows in the United States (one observer says one hundred and fifty million) cannot have been without some effect on the populations of native birds; the house sparrow in Britain is dominant over other small garden species and drives them away from feeding tables (Plate 24, p. 221). It should, however, not be overlooked that at the time the house sparrow was introduced into America the country was suffering a great biological upheaval that in itself was making those areas most regularly observed by man more unsuitable for the indigenous species, none of which was anything like so well suited to the urbanised habitat that was being created; without the sparrow this niche would probably be much less fully exploited than it is to-day. It should also be noted that there has been a general decrease over the same period in the numbers of many small birds, such as the warblers, with which the sparrow does not compete—the most probable cause is a decrease in the numbers of insects as a result of improved hygiene, weed clearance and more recently from intensive spraying against insect pests—yet urban areas support large populations of starlings and blackbirds that are mainly animal feeders: if populations of birds are controlled by food supply, as seems to be the generally held view, then the house sparrow can hardly be held responsible for the decrease in the numbers of insect-eating species.

On the credit side it is claimed that during the breeding season they consume a lot of insects that would otherwise do considerable damage and it must not be overlooked that their presence in cities and towns gives pleasure to many. The toll of insects is not inconsiderable and as young are in the nest from late April to August or September it continues for about a third of the year; in addition I have also frequently seen the adults themselves feeding on blackfly in October. E. R. Kalmbach in a study of the relationship between birds and the introduced alfalfa weevil (*Hypera postica*) in Salt Lake Valley, U.S.A., showed that the (English) sparrow was one of the most effective bird enemies of this pest, these weevils accounting for nearly thirty per cent of the food of the adults in June as well as being fed to the young; an estimate showed that single broods of sparrows were daily destroying nearly two thousand weevil larvae. Other reports are less striking, though Kalmbach also rates the sparrow highly as an enemy of destructive grasshoppers and locusts. In a few cases the insects identified in stomach analyses have been divided into noxious, neutral and beneficial to man, but it is clear from the results that the insects taken depend only on availability and it would be wrong to draw any conclusions of general applicability from the few data published, though clearly some insects that man is pleased to call noxious must be taken in all parts of the bird's range. Even admitting this the question of how far birds are ever effective in controlling insects is still a matter for debate and one rather outside the scope of this book.

On the aesthetic pleasure given by these prolific occupants of built-up areas there is much less doubt. This point of view was put forward strongly by W. Rhodes in America in 1877: "I imagine no live Yankee would wish now to be without the life and animation of the house sparrow in his great cities. They are like gas in a town—a sign of progress. I admit the bird is a little blackguard—fond of low society and full of fight, stealing, and love-making—but he is death on insects, fond of citizen life, and in every way suitable to be an inhabitant of the New World." Or as Robert Lynd says: "He has no music for the traffic to drown—no bright plumage for the smoke to blacken. He is a little parasite, who can pick up a living where a more sensitive bird would starve. He is cheeky, Cockney, irrepressible. . . . How charming a little dancer he is as he pops in scores and fifties round a Londoner who has bread—hops backwards and forwards like a marionette or like someone whose feet have been tied together for fun, or like a small child hopping up and down in sheer excitement. He may not, as an individual, be as confiding as the robin. But the robins do not come dancing round a human being in families like the family of the old woman who lived in a shoe." Much of this is highly emotional: when trapping was carried out in an effort to reduce the numbers of sparrows in the stores mentioned in Chapter 10, "bird-lovers" set the birds free when the authorities had their backs turned; F. Preiser in his investigation, which demanded the setting up of a large number of traps, found that farmers killed any trapped birds they came across, whereas "bird-lovers" released them.

Now having reviewed the evidence, what sort of a balance can we strike? As in so many of these discussions on the economic importance of wild animals there can be no clear-cut answer. So much depends on the numbers of the animal and where it occurs— as Kalmbach states: "Unless the species has an effect that is regularly and seriously injurious to advocate indiscriminate destruction is as fallacious from an economic standpoint as to urge absolute protection for forms that may locally or periodically become destructive." He concludes by saying: ". . . the English sparrow as a species must constantly be looked upon with suspicion. Its misdeeds frequently call for measures of control; but it must not be forgotten that nature in its complexity may locally present the exception rather than the rule. Indiscriminate and unlimited control of any creature having even a few redeeming qualities may easily frustrate the basic object sought."

Southern arrives at the following conclusions after his comprehensive review of the position:

(i) In arable land the adult sparrow eats a large percentage of grain.

(ii) Most of this, except during the harvest period, is waste grain or chicken food.

(iii) In some parts of the world weed seeds are largely eaten (40–80 per cent), but even so, if the density is excessive, the sparrow may be a crop pest, destroying up to 30 per cent of crops.

(iv) In addition, the sparrow may act partly as a disseminator of weed seeds (to what extent is not accurately known at present).

(v) In suburban, park and garden and fruit-growing areas the sparrow will eat a certain amount of corn (30 per cent), though most of this is probably waste. The amount of insects in the diet, largely species harmful economically, increases in these areas and the sparrow does a fair proportion of good here.

(vi) Young sparrows in the nest are fed mostly upon insects, mainly harmful species, but have already switched to a vegetable diet by the time they are fledged. In exceptional cases large numbers of insect pests may be taken by sparrows to feed their young and the adults may eat numbers also.

On balance, I feel that the house sparrows living in rural districts can probably be regarded as harmful to man's interests, especially in those areas that support a large population density; in towns the case is not really sufficiently strong against sparrows to regard them as enemies.

The implication of the 1954 Bird Protection Act, which places the house sparrow in the list of twenty species appearing in the Second Schedule—the blacklist of birds that may be killed or taken at any time of the year—is that it is recognised as an undesirable species. However, even if we admit this, the question whether some measure of control would be worth-while still remains and, if so, what form it should take. While no active steps are at present being taken against sparrows in the British Isles, a considerable campaign has been mounted in Germany since the war. We have already seen in Chapter 14 that the density of sparrows in parts of Germany is extremely high and the following passage translated from the German is typical of the prefatory remarks that have appeared in many of the publications devoted to sparrow control: "From thousands of letters from all circles of the population, especially of the rural population, there comes the alarming information that the damage which the house and tree sparrows cause each year in our grain fields, is greater by far than was supposed. In many letters from peasant circles it was asserted that the sparrow plague is so great that the grain harvest is endangered. From the echo, which our measures against the sparrow brought out, it is clear that the numbers in many districts are as frightening as in Hesse and that we must now use all the means at our disposal all over Germany to control the sparrow plague." Numerous experiments have been conducted by Bird and Plant Protection Organisations and Agricultural Colleges on the best methods of trapping, poisoning, destruction of nests and other means of keeping the numbers under control. In the last few years several large-scale poisonings using treated grain have been carried out in the winter months in various parts of Germany. After intensive poisoning in winter it was estimated that the population could be reduced as much as seventy-five per cent, but Preiser showed in his extensive ringing experiments that there was a significant ingress of birds from surrounding populations into these "sparrow-poor" places, so that if an overall reduction in numbers is to be achieved, poisoning would have to be conducted on a vast scale and continued from year to year. Whether this would be practicable or for that matter economically justifiable is quite another question. In small isolated communities some control of sparrow numbers could be effected in this way because of the sedentary nature of the bird; over large populous areas it is extremely doubtful whether sufficient effort could be sustained to be worth-while. It is probable that more damage is caused to grain by insects, virus disease and other pests and effort is probably more profitably devoted to their control than to the control of sparrows. The only really effective method of controlling the damage caused by the large grain-field flocks would be to reduce the amount of food available to the birds at other times of the year by discouraging the deliberate putting out of bread for birds in gardens and to deny the birds access to food put out for hens in poultry runs. Whether effective measures of this type could be put into practice is somewhat doubtful.

From China there comes recently a report of control measures against sparrows (in this case the tree sparrow, which is the "house sparrow" of China), which could well have come from one of Kai Lung's tales rather than the sober pages of the *China Youth Daily*. Students, children and soldiers were organised in many parts of China to fire guns and beat gongs for periods of three days so that the sparrows could not rest and eventually fell down from exhaustion and were destroyed. It is claimed that in Peking three million people took part; fifteen thousand birds had been killed in the first three hours and one hundred and five thousand in the complete campaign. In Shantung Province two million eight hundred thousand sparrows were killed in the first half of the winter of 1955–6 by shooting and poisoning. One lad in a Manchurian village, who accounted for thirty-six nesting sparrows one night, was widely extolled in the papers and designated a "sparrow-killing activist".

Where sparrows are a nuisance in stores and other buildings some effort towards control may be justified. The solution to the problem appears to lie in getting the work people to co-operate in denying the birds food, keeping windows and doors shut as much as possible, particularly just before roosting time, which in the case of the sparrow is about half-an-hour before sunset, and closing up the small holes that give access to nesting sites inside the buildings. In a depot that I know the concentration of sparrows inside the buildings grew to such an extent that the management were asked to do something about it. Various control measures were adopted but these were frustrated to some extent by the "bird-lovers" who encouraged the birds and provided them with food. The problem was eventually reduced to manageable proportions by blocking up as many of the entrance points as possible and was greatly aided by a tawny owl and sparrow-hawk, which on different occasions took up residence inside the buildings and lived easily on the large number of birds. These two birds certainly ate many sparrows but probably reduced the numbers more by scaring them away. It is perhaps not surprising that an owl should come into a building in this way when it could roost without disturbance during the day and live on the roosting sparrows at night, but it is remarkable that a sparrow-hawk should come inside an occupied building after the

sparrows living there and, what is more, that it should resist
attempts by the men inside the building to chase it out. Although
effective in reducing the problem it might be difficult to induce
birds of prey to help out, though perhaps a falconer might be called
in to lend a hand in cases of need—the effect of a single sparrow-
hawk on the large roost of sparrows in Egypt quoted in Chapter 10
shows what one bird can do in a short time; certainly this was the
solution proposed by the Duke of Wellington when Queen Victoria
complained in 1851 of the numbers of sparrows inside the Crystal
Palace, though history does not relate if the advice was taken.

CHAPTER 19

THE SECRET OF SUCCESS

WE COME now to the end of our story. What are we to make of this bird? There is no doubt that it is a most successful animal and has not yet reached its peak. A dramatic increase in its distribution has taken place in the last century and this phase in the sparrow's history is by no means at an end. Apart from further increases in range and numbers in Siberia and South America that will certainly occur, I think that it is inevitable that the bird will soon extend into China and may well colonise Western Australia despite man's efforts to keep it out.

However, quite apart from this colonisation that is still going on, changes are also taking place in parts where the house sparrow has been present for some time. There are several factors responsible for these changes and it is necessary to identify them if we are to understand how the sparrow is to be affected on balance. There is good evidence to show that a decrease in numbers occurred in many parts of its range in the 1920's. This is almost certainly to be associated with the decrease in food available for it as the horse was gradually ousted from towns and the population density adjusted itself to the new level of food supplies. Much food, however, is put out in towns for birds and this allows a very large population of house sparrows to maintain itself. A more recent factor that is also tending to reduce numbers is the gradual decline in the resident human population in the centres of large towns, which are becoming more and more sterile and arid and less attractive to sparrows; in these business areas the wider ranging feral pigeon is now becoming the only bird of importance apart from the starlings that come in from the surrounding countryside to roost at night. These two factors have certainly had their effect on the number of sparrows in North America but there is evidence that the decline had already set in there before they could have been of importance. It took some years for the house sparrow to become established in

America but once this occurred there was a tremendous increase in numbers, which, in the absence of the factors that in the older-established parts of its range act as controls, resulted in an explosion giving abnormally high population densities for a temporary period. This was, however, only a short-term effect and the decline to more normal densities had already set in when it was accelerated by the factors that were causing a decrease elsewhere. A similar swing may have taken place after the introductions to New Zealand and Australia though this does not appear to have been recorded. Rapid increases resulting in abnormal populations are less likely to have occurred in other countries where the bird was introduced, as these have not been modified to anything like the same extent by man to the sort of urban-agricultural complex that is so attractive to the house sparrow.

Offsetting these factors that result in decreases in numbers there is the extraordinary growth of urbanisation that is taking place all over the world, increasing the type of environment that the house sparrow is better adapted to than any other bird species. The increase in building, growth of towns and built-up areas is certainly increasing the total population of house sparrows in the British Isles and will inevitably do so in other parts of the bird's range where similar changes are taking place.

Herein lies of course the key to the sparrow's success. It has become adapted to living close to man and yet it has not become so highly specialised that it is restricted to a very limited niche. It is catholic in its food requirements, living equally well on scraps or grain, supplemented by grass seeds and insects as the occasion provides. Again in the matter of nest-sites its choice leads to no limitation. Above all it is very tolerant of disturbance by man, though it could never be described as tame. I think that on balance it is becoming less and less a bird of agriculture and more and more a commensal of urbanised man; where agriculture and built-up areas meet it finds its greatest scope. It is also remarkably free from successful enemies; the cat, and birds of prey, like the sparrow-hawk and the owls, are the principal ones but they do not account for a significant proportion of the birds except in a few rather restricted areas.

Another possible reason for the house sparrow's success is its adaptability. The building of roost nests is a case in point. As we have seen this habit becomes commoner in high latitudes and enables the birds to remain as residents when otherwise they would probably be unable to survive the long cold winter nights. The use of tree sites for nesting is also interesting. Holes in buildings are definitely the preferred site in this country, as shown by the way in which the tree nests in my rural colony were quickly deserted in favour of nest-boxes when these were put up; tree nests are evidently used when the number of available nesting-holes is less than the number of breeding pairs that the available food will support. This flexibility in the choice of nest-site is obviously of advantage; other hole-nesters such as tits and pied flycatchers do not possess the same adaptability.

It is also quick in exploiting new situations. In the First World War it was often about in the trenches and was one of the commonest birds of the battlefield even away from buildings. And it was one of the first birds to return to villages after an action. Again in Australia the instances of breeding away from man and the extreme diversity of habitats the house sparrow occupies in New Zealand gives further evidence of the bird's general vigour and adaptability.

The main reason for the success of the introduction of the house sparrow to various parts of the world is that it was adapted to an ecological niche that has not been exploited by any other bird and thus met little resistance. Most of the ecological niches in America were occupied by the time that Europeans began to colonise the continent and very few introduced species, apart from the sparrow and starling, have been successful there. Absence of competitors in associated niches may have allowed the bird to spread into rather different habitats from that occupied in the normal parts of its range, for example, into scrub country in New Zealand and Australia. New Zealand in particular had a rather poor indigenous fauna and several introduced European species have succeeded there.

In feeding habits too house sparrows seem to show great variety. They appear to be just as much at home feeding on the shore along the tide line or among the barrows in a railway station as they do at a ripening field of corn. They are also quick to exploit new sources of food—a flush of caterpillars, which soon attracts a flock of sparrows, the taking of squashed insects from the radiator grilles of cars and, most interesting, the collection of insects attracted to lights at a time of night when the birds would normally be roosting; the latter has been seen both in America and India. Another American record is of sparrows collecting flies from shop windows in the early morning where they had settled the previous evening when they were warm but were now listless in the cold morning air.

A further reason for the sparrow's undoubted success may lie in its superior intelligence. I realise that I am on dangerous ground in attributing intelligence to a bird, but there are differences in the learning abilities of different species, as well as differences in the abilities of the individuals of the same species, which would confer an advantage. J. P. Porter in a study of the psychology of the house sparrow subjected captive birds to a variety of situations in which the bird had to solve a problem or to make the correct choice from a number of containers to obtain food. Two types of problem were used: in one the bird had to unlatch a door of a wire cage in which the food was visible to obtain access to it; in the other the food was visible at the centre of a simple maze and the bird had to find its way to it. In the second group of situations the food was located in one of a number of containers which were marked in different ways; in different tests the containers were distinguished by position in a series, by colour, by shape and by different designs. In all of the tests, apart from the one in which the containers were of different shape, the birds rapidly profited by experience and quickly learned to find their way to the food or select the correct container. Only one bird was subjected to the "shape" test and either she was not able to differentiate between shapes or her association with the position of the container rather than its shape were too strong. The results of these tests suggest that the sparrow's method of learning is one of trial and error—there was no evidence of reasoning or thought-out behaviour. The main points of interest were the speed with which, once the correct solution had been found, it was learnt and was even remembered for a period of days when the bird was not re-tested, and the persistence with which the birds attempted to find food. Both of these characteristics would obviously be of great value to the bird in real life. Mrs. Kipps also remarks on the pertinacity of her pet sparrow Clarence and how he learned a number of tricks that she taught him "with extraordinary ease and rapidity". Porter also carried out tests with a cowbird, vesper sparrow, passenger pigeon and domestic pigeon; the cowbird had a similar learning ability to the house sparrow, but the others were inferior. Similar tests with monkeys and white rats showed that the method and rate of learning of the house sparrow was comparable with that of the higher vertebrates. This is illustrated in Fig. 35, p. 238, which is taken from Porter's earlier paper and compares the rate of learning of house sparrow, monkey and white rat in maze tests; the time to get to the food in the centre of the maze in the first trial is taken as standard and in the succeeding trials is expressed as a percentage of this. The Figure shows a very similar pattern of learning for the three animals.

Viscount Grey in *The Charm of Birds* describes a natural experiment that contrasts the cleverness and learning ability of the house sparrow with that of the chaffinch. A basket of bread, which was fed to the waterfowl, was kept in a greenhouse. Several pairs of chaffinches nested near the greenhouse but, although they fed their young on bread when available, they failed to find their way in. After a lapse of some years a pair of house sparrows nested about fifty yards from the greenhouse and very soon they discovered how to get to the bread through the ventilator. As soon as anyone entered they flew out immediately without any hesitation. Even with the sparrows showing them the way the chaffinches did not learn to copy them.

L. S. V. Venables has described the behaviour of house sparrows at a Heligoland trap on the Isle of May, which suggests a high order of learning ability. The only cover on the island has been arranged at the entrance to the trap; in addition to the migrant species visiting the island many of the resident birds used regularly to seek this cover. However, while birds like thrushes and pipits were readily driven from the cover into the trap and were caught many times, the sparrows and starlings had learned to fly

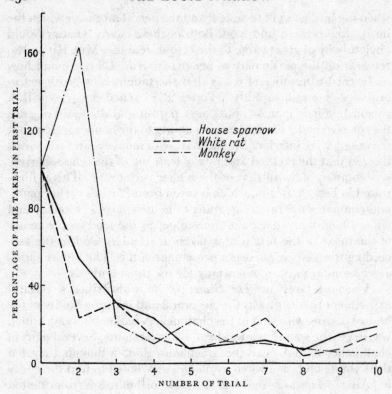

FIG. 35. Comparison of performance of house sparrow, white rat and monkey in maze tests. (After J. P. Porter.)

out over the heads of the beaters. Even when a trail of bread was laid into the trap these two species, apart from a few individuals that were regularly caught and seemed incapable of learning, would fly straight towards the noise and apparent danger of the beaters, and escape by flying out above their outstretched hands. This behaviour was in complete contrast to that of the other birds, which fled away from the noise into the trap. Venables remarks that if the object of the exercise had been to wring the necks of the birds instead of to ring their legs, this behaviour would have been of clear advantage to the sparrows. Another species that has learned to avoid being trapped is the wren, though the technique adopted is different—this bird merely lies doggo until the ringers have passed and then makes its escape behind their backs.

J. F. Brenckle has remarked that the house sparrow learns more quickly than other species to find its way out of funnel traps and I have found when using such a trap it pays to secure any sparrow that enters as quickly as possible; while other garden species can be left for long periods and seem unable to get out, most adult sparrows escape if left for more than a minute or two. In my experience house sparrows more commonly make their escape from handling cages than other species. Brenckle has described even more astonishing behaviour in a circular, multi-cell trap which, at the centre where the apices of the cells met, had a dish of water with an equal segment in each cell. On being trapped sparrows regularly attempted to escape by diving into the three-and-a-half inch deep water and swimming as much as twelve inches under the water to get from one cell to another; no other species that he caught in this trap attempted similar behaviour.

House sparrows probably did not work out for themselves the way to obtain milk from milk-bottles but presumably learnt this by copying blue tits. It is interesting that after tits, who evolved this behaviour, house sparrows were recorded as the next commonest species doing it, though of course living close to man they would probably have more opportunities than other species. Porter also got the impression from his experiments with house sparrows that they were able to profit not only from their own experience but also by watching and imitating other birds. Many observers have remarked on the way that trap-shyness is communicated through a flock of sparrows in the wild (at first when traps are put out a few sparrows from the local flock are caught but soon they no longer enter the traps) and this seems to suggest some form of communication or profiting by the experience of others. It is also noteworthy how quickly sparrows learn to avoid an automatic trap when it is set but readily enter when it is not. Observations have been made from time to time of house sparrows soaking hard crusts in water before eating them. This could be an accidently acquired habit but even then is an interesting example of learning.

Provided intelligence is restricted to the limited field of learning ability we can keep clear of dangerous ground; however, some observations on the bird seem to show something more than mere trial and error learning and suggest some appreciation of the situation, in other words, the use of intelligence. The fact that so much of a bird's life is based on instinctive behaviour patterns does not necessarily exclude the possibility of some intelligent action. As an example of this I shall describe the actions of a pair of house sparrows that were nesting in a ventilator in a cavity wall of an office occupied by a colleague of mine. Both the outside and inside ventilator grilles had rusted so that there were holes through which sparrows could pass. The nest completely filled the space between the grilles, the entrance being at the hole in the grille leading to the outside. After the parents had been feeding young in the nest for a few days the owner of the office began to object to the noise created by the young birds and attempted to dislodge the nest; he only succeeded, however, in completely blocking up the access to the nest from the outside of the building. The parents then did an extraordinary thing; almost immediately they entered the office through an open window, made a new entrance through the wall of the nest exposed to the hole of the inside grille and began to feed the young from the inside of the building. As far as was known the sparrows had never entered the office before and had not used the inside ventilator as a route to the nest.

We must be careful not to push these examples too far; there are many times when it is evident that any intelligence or reasoning is completely absent—for example, when pairs attempt to breed in holes that are obviously (to the human observer) too small. Nevertheless instances of the sort that I have described do indicate signs of intelligence and certainly suggest a real difference in the levels of behaviour between species that may give one an advantage over another—it is perhaps not without relevance that the brain weight of the house sparrow is proportionately higher (one gramme or 4·3 per cent) than that of many other species. This capacity in the house sparrow together with its adaptability and association with man almost certainly plays some part in accounting for its very remarkable success. Another animal that has had a similar success to that of the house sparrow is the brown rat; it took approximately the same time to cover the North American continent, having arrived about fifty years before the sparrow. It is perhaps no coincidence that it too is a symbiote of urban and agricultural man as well as having a reputation among mammals for superior intelligence.

THE SPARROWS
AND THEIR NEAR RELATIVES

THE SPARROWS belong to the Passeriform order and are a sub-family of
the weaver-birds as shown below.

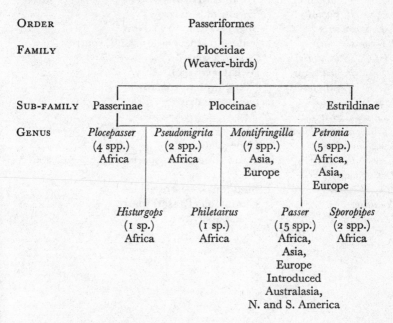

| ORDER | Passeriformes |
| FAMILY | Ploceidae (Weaver-birds) |

| SUB-FAMILY | Passerinae | Ploceinae | Estrildinae |

| GENUS | *Plocepasser* (4 spp.) Africa | *Pseudonigrita* (2 spp.) Africa | *Montifringilla* (7 spp.) Asia, Europe | *Petronia* (5 spp.) Africa, Asia, Europe |
| | *Histurgops* (1 sp.) Africa | *Philetairus* (1 sp.) Africa | *Passer* (15 spp.) Africa, Asia, Europe Introduced Australasia, N. and S. America | *Sporopipes* (2 spp.) Africa |

Passer contains the following species. Insufficient is known about
inter-relations within the genus to arrange the members in a logical
sequence and, in accordance with the lead given by R. E. Moreau, I
have listed them alphabetically in order to avoid any unintended
implications. Species that have been assimilated and scientific names
that have been superseded are given in parentheses, as are also alternative vernacular names. The approximate distributions of the species
are given in Fig. 36, pp. 245-7.

P. ammodendri	Saxaul sparrow
P. castanopterus	Somali sparrow
P. domesticus	House (English) sparrow
(incl. *P. italiae*)	(Italian sparrow)
P. eminibey	Chestnut (Emin Bey's) sparrow
(*Sorella eminibey*)	
P. flaveolus	Pegu (olive-crowned or Phengyi) sparrow
P. griseus	Grey sparrow
(incl. *P. gongonensis*)	(Parrot-billed sparrow)
(*P. suahelicus*)	(Swahili sparrow)
(*P. swainsonii*)	(Swainson's sparrow)
P. hispaniolensis	Spanish (willow) sparrow
P. iagoensis	Rufous (Cape Verde Island) sparrow
(incl. *P. insularis*)	(Socotra sparrow)
(*P. motitensis*)	(Great sparrow)
(*P. rufocinctus*)	(Kenya rufous sparrow)
P. luteus	Golden sparrow
(*Auripasser luteus*)	
(*Auripasser euchlorus*)	
P. melanurus	Cape sparrow
P. moabiticus	Scrub (Dead Sea) sparrow
P. montanus	Tree sparrow
P. pyrrhonotus	Sind jungle sparrow
P. rutilans	Cinnamon (Russet) sparrow
P. simplex	Desert sparrow.

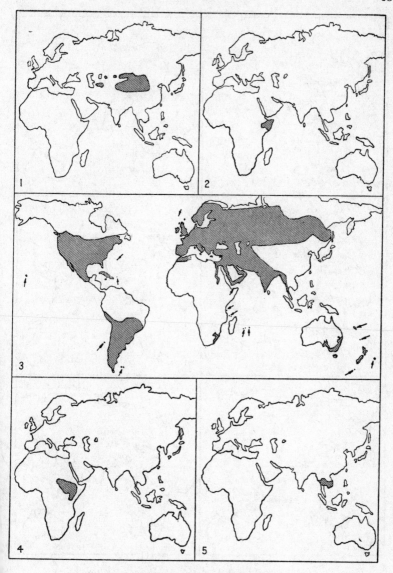

FIG. 36. Distribution of *Passer* species.

1. *P. ammodendri*   4. *P. emimibey*
2. *P. castanopterus*
3. *P. domesticus*   5. *P. flaveolus*

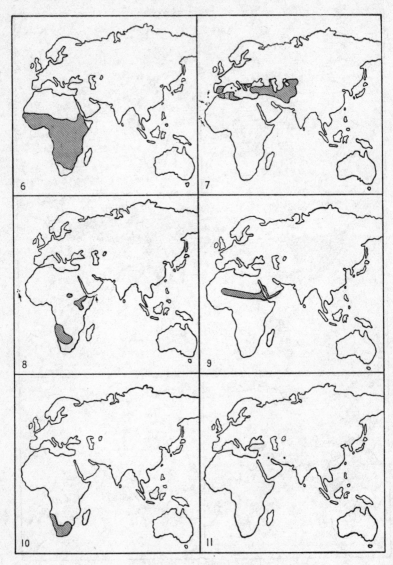

FIG. 36. Distribution of *Passer* species (continued)

6. *P. griseus*   9. *P. luteus*
7. *P. hispaniolensis* 10. *P. melanurus*
8. *P. iagoensis*   11. *P. moabiticus*

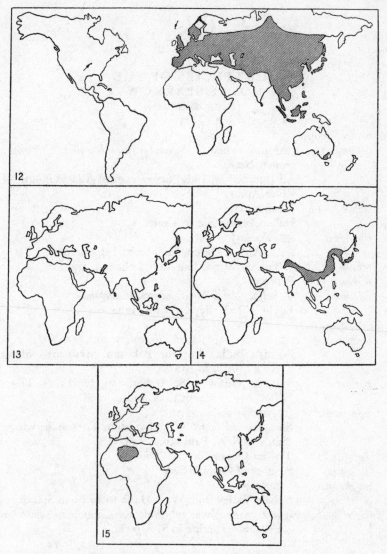

FIG. 36. Distribution of *Passer* species (concluded)

12. *P. montanus*   14. *P. rutilans*
13. *P. pyrrhonotus*   15. *P. simplex*

SUB-SPECIES OF THE HOUSE SPARROW
(*Passer domesticus*)

domesticus-group:

domesticus	(≡*hostilis, diniz, balaerobericus, baicalicus sibiricus, semiretschiensis*).
	All Europe (ex. Italy) across central Asia to mouth of River Amur.
italiae	(≡*schiebeli*)
	Italy, Corsica, Sicily, Crete.
tingitanus	(≡*adhasvar*)
	N.W. Africa, Cyrenaica (absent Tripolitania).
biblicus	S. Turkey, Syria, Palestine, Lebanon, Iraq.
persicus	Persia.
niloticus	(≡*halfae, alexandrinus, aegypticus, cheprini*)
	Egypt, Nile Valley to Wadi Halfa.

indicus-group:

indicus	(≡*confucius, soror, nigricollis, enigmaticus, buryi*)
	Burma, India, Ceylon, Pakistan, westwards along S. coast of Asia to Arabia.
parkini	Summer visitor to S. Afghanistan, Ladak, S. Tibet, Nepal; winter visitor to N. India.
bactrianus	(≡*griseogularis*)
	Summer visitor to N. Afghanistan, Turkestan; winter visitor to N.W. Pakistan.
hufufae	Trucial Oman.
hyrcanus	S. shore of Caspian Sea.
rufidorsalis	(≡*arboreus*)
	S. Nile Valley from Wadi Halfa to 12°N. in Sudan.

flükigeri (≡*bergeri*) is a name given to stable *domesticus* × *hispaniolensis* hybrids occurring in S. Algeria.

HOUSE SPARROW STATISTICS

		♂♂	♀♀
Body Temperature		106·7°F.	
Heart rate		800 per minute	
Breathing frequency at rest		94 per min. at −55°F.	
		200 per min. at 93°F.	
Wing beats		13 per second	
Speed of flight: cruising		24 m.p.h.	
maximum		33 m.p.h.	
Frequency range of hearing		675 to 18,000 c/s	
Greatest known age: in wild		11½ years	
captive		12 years	
Winglength (Great Britain)*:	range	71–81 mm.	69–78 mm.
	mean	76 mm.	74 mm.
		(400 birds)	(150 birds)
Tail length	mean	55 mm.	52 mm.
Bill length	mean	12 mm.	11·5 mm.
Tarsus length	mean	19·5 mm.	19 mm.
Weight (Germany)	range	24·5–39·5 g.	24·5–38·5 g.
	mean	30·5 g.	30 g.
		(2,000 birds)	(2,000 birds)
Egg size (Great Britain)	mean	22·5 × 15·7 mm.	
	max.	25·3 × 15 mm.	
		23·5 × 16 mm.	
	min.	19·7 × 15·5 mm.	
		22·5 × 14·5 mm.	
Number of feathers		3,100 to 3,600	
Clutch size (Great Britain)		1 to 7, mean 4·10 (702 clutches)	
No. of clutches per year (Gt. Britain)		1 to 4, mean 2·1 (90 pairs)	
Incubation period (Great Britain)		9 to 18 days, mode 12 days (98 clutches)	
Nestling period (Great Britain)		11 to 19 days, mode 18 days (83 clutches)	

* From other parts of its range wing lengths for ♂♂ have been recorded from 69 mm. up to 85 mm.; means range from 72 to 81 mm.

Hatching success (Great Britain)   71% eggs laid (2,774 eggs)
Fledging success (Great Britain)   74% young hatched (1,401
                                           young)
Breeding success** (Great Britain)   50% eggs laid (2,109 eggs)

** This is based on the overall success of eggs laid; the breeding success obtained by multiplying the hatching success and fledging success figures, which are obtained from slightly different samples, is 53%.

MORE DISTANT RINGING RECOVERIES

Juv	20.6.46	Brynsciencyn, Anglesey: 53° 10′N 4° 17′W	21 m.
	–.3.47	Llandudno: 53° 19′N 3° 51′W	N.E.
Ad ♀	2.1.51	Conisborough, Yorks.: 53° 29′N 1° 12′W	10 m.
	ca 7.2.54	Cudworth, Yorks.: 53° 25′N 1° 25′W	N.W.
F.G.	22.3.52	Flixton, Lancs.: 53° 26′N 2° 24′W	11 m.
	(12.1.56)	Lower Ince, nr. Wigan	N.W.
F.G.	14.8.52	Gt. Budworth, Ches.: 53° 18′N 2° 28′W	15 m.
			N.E.
Pull.	23.6.54	St. Osyth, Essex: 51° 47′N 1° 04′E	30 m.
	18.3.55	Cooling Marsh, Kent	S.W.
Ad ♀	11.7.54	Monkstown, Co. Dublin	25 m.
	12.11.54	Enfield, Co. Kildare	W.
♀	3.10.55	Dungeness, Kent: 50° 54′N 0° 59′E	26 m.
	12.9.58	Walmer, Kent: 51° 12′N 1° 23′E	N.E.
F.G. ♀	30.12.55	Spurn, Yorks.: 53° 35′N 0° 06′E	16 m.
	(10.3.56)	Paull, Yorks.: 53° 42′N 0° 12′W	W.N.W.
F.G. ♂	30.12.55	Spurn, Yorks.	14 m.
	9.7.56	Hilston, Yorks.: 53° 47′N 0° 05′W	N.W.
♂	4.3.56	Spurn, Yorks.	27 m.
	23.3.56	Nunkeeling, nr. Driffield	W.N.W.
F.G.	13.4.57	Portland Bill, Dorset: 50° 31′N 2° 27′W	58 m.
	(7.12.58)	E. Portlemouth, Devon.: 50° 14′N 3° 47′W	W.S.W.
Juv	22.6.57	Knaresborough, Yorks.: 54° 01′N 1° 29′W	11 m.
	20.5.58	Hessay, Yorks.: 53° 57′N 1° 09′W	E.
♀	16.10.57	Spurn, Yorks.	57 m.
	3.7.59	Middleton: 54° 15′N 0° 46′W	N.W.
F.G. ♀	26.7.59	Portland, Dorset: 50° 31′N 2° 27′W	70 m.
	14.2.60	Cherbourg, France: 49° 39′N 1° 40′W	S.S.E.
	4.11.27	Wetteren, Belgium: 51°N 3° 51′E	10 m.
	end '31	St. Gillis: 51° 02′N 4° 07′E	E.
Pull	1.8.33	Wildert, Belgium: 51° 25′N 4° 28′E	12 m.
		Hoogstraten: 51° 24′N 4° 44′E	E.
	2.9.53	Camargue, France: 43° 30′N 4° 40′E	20 m.
	29.1.54	Croix Sainte	S.E.

Ad ♂	27.11.53	Camargue, France	185 m.
	28.4.54	Alpignano, Italy: 45° 05′N 7° 30′E	N.E.
	30.11.53	Camargue, France	34 m.
	12.12.54	Montpezat St. Mamert: 43° 54′N 4° 11′E	N.W.
Ad ♂	30.12.53	Camargue, France	40 m.
	12.12.54	St. Geniès: 43° 56′N 4° 13′E	N.W.
♂	20.12.53	Camargue, France	185 m.
	9.1.55	Sino d'Alba, Italy: 44° 30′N 8°E	N.E.
♂	24.10.30	Heligoland: 54° 10′N 7° 51′E	40 m.
	14.11.30	Büsum, Germany: 54° 08′N 8° 52′E	E.
♀	14.11.34	Heligoland	38 m.
	15.11.34	Amrumbank, Germany: 54° 41′N 8° 19′E	N.N.E.
♂	14.2.35	Heligoland	38 m.
	12.8.35	Wogenmannenburg: 54° 23′N 8° 41′E	E.N.E.
♂	13.10.35	Litschin, Germany: 51° 22′N 14° 25′E	93 m.
	17.1.36	Waltersdorf: 51° 01′N 12° 23′E	W.S.W.
Juv ♀	30.7.36	Bonn, Germany: 50° 44′N 7° 04′E	25 m.
	5.11.36	Brunohl: 50° 59′N 7° 52′E	N.E.
Juv	7.8.37	Heligoland	60 m.
	10.6.38	Niebüll: 54° 47′N 8° 50′E	N.E.
♀	–5–	Kiel, Germany: 54° 16′N 10° 8′E	29 m.
	–5–	—	
♀	20.6.52	Echterdingen, Germany: 48° 41′N 9° 13′E	280 m.
	–.3.53	Lyon, France: 45° 46′N 4° 50′E	S.W.
♂	6.8.52	Echterdingen	20 m.
	29.3.53	Genkingen: 48° 24′N 9° 11′E	S.
♀	14.8.52	Echterdingen	53 m.
	20.11.52	Hausach: 48° 17′N 8° 13′E	S.W.
♀	14.8.52	Reidenberg: 48° 43′N 9° 13′E	11 m.
	4.4.54	Eltingen	W.N.W.
♀	22.8.52	Echterdingen	11 m.
	25.10.52	Stammheim	N.
♀	10.6.53	Echterdingen	340 m.
	3.1.54	Livron-sur-Drôme: 44° 47′N 4° 52′E	S.W.
♂	9.10.53	Reidenberg	16 m.
	15.7.54	Dettingen: 48° 30′N 9° 21′E	S.S.E.
Juv.	10.7.52	Bonn 50° 43′N 7° 6′E	38 m.
	26.6.53	Wenden 50° 56′N 7° 50′E	N.E.
Juv	10.8.54	Kiel	36 m.
	4.9.54	Itzehoe: 53° 56′N 9° 31′E	S.W.

Juv ♀	3.6.48	Steinkjer, Norway: 63° 59′N 11° 40′E	38 m.
	18.6.49	Overhalla	E.
Pull	24.6.36	Proskau, Poland: 50° 35′N 17° 53′E	25 m.
	3.7.36	Langenbrück: 50° 18′N 17° 31′E	S.W.
♂	24.1.36	Rossitten: 55° 10′N 20° 51′E	41 m.
	15.11.36	Siedling Polennen: 54° 48′N 20° 03′E	S.W.
	29.10.36	Windenburg	12 m.
	8.1.37	Mestellen	N.E.
♀	24.9.37	Memel	66 m.
	7.2.38	Domnau: 54° 26′N 20° 48′E	S.S.W.

RATIO OF THE SEXES
IN THE HOUSE SPARROW

LARGELY as a result of large-scale poisonings of house sparrows in Germany in the last few years much information has become available on the proportions of the sexes. This is summarised in the table below together with some results from the U.S.A. based on sight observations.

Locality	Time of year	No. of birds examined	♂♂ Number	♂♂ Proportion	Sample	χ²
North Rhine-Westphalia, Germany	3/52	1,276	650	54·7%	poisoned birds	1
Saxony-Anhalt, Germany	12/52 to 3/53 and 1/54 to 2/54	20,931	11,130	53·2%	,,	84
Württemburg, Germany	11/54 to 3/55	8.112	4,080	50·3%	,,	1
Thuringia, Germany	1953–7	397	214	53·9%	collected nestlings	2·4
New York, U.S.A.		7,754	4,243	54·7%	sight records	69

For the results to indicate statistically that males outnumber females, χ^2 must be greater than 12 (p=0·001); it will be seen that this is the case with the large sample from Saxony-Anhalt and for the American observations (although sight records are obviously less convincing than those based on dissection, it is more probable that young males will be wrongly identified as females than vice versa, hence the results are probably reliable). We can conclude that the sexes are almost equal in numbers with a slight tendency for males to preponderate.

SCIENTIFIC NAMES OF BIRDS MENTIONED IN THE TEXT
(*Names of birds in the sub-family Passerinae are given in Appendix I*)

Fulmar
Fulmaris glacialis
Heron
Ardea cinerea
Mallard
Anas platyrhynchos
Sparrow-hawk
Accipiter nisus
Peregrine
Falco peregrinus
Kestrel
Falco tinnunculus
Partridge
Perdix perdix
Pheasant
Phasianus colchicus
Moorhen
Gallinula chloropus
Black-headed Gull
Larus ridibundus
Town Pigeon
Columba livia
Wood Pigeon
Columba palumbus
Passenger Pigeon
Columba migratoria
Cuckoo
Cuculus canoris
Barn Owl
Tyto alba
Tawny Owl
Strix aluco
Long-eared Owl
Asio otus

Whip-poor-will
Caprimulgus vociferus
Swift
Apus apus
Kingfisher
Alcedo atthis
Lesser-spotted Woodpecker
Dendrocopus minor
Skylark
Alauda arvensis
Swallow
Hirundo rustica
Cliff Swallow
Petrochelidon albifrons
Fairy Martin
Hylochelidon ariel
House Martin
Delichon urbica
Sand Martin
Riparia riparia
Carrion Crow
Corvus corone
Rook
Corvus frugilegus
Jackdaw
Corvus monedula
Magpie
Pica pica
Blue Tit
Parus caeruleus
Nuthatch
Sitta europaea
Tree Creeper
Certhia familiaris

Wren
  Troglodytes troglodytes
Mistle Thrush
  Turdus viscivorus
Song Thrush
  Turdus ericetorum
Blackbird
  Turdus merula
Nightingale
  Luscinia megarhyncha
Robin
  Erithacus rubecula
Spotted Flycatcher
  Muscicapa striata
Dunnock
  Prunella modularis
Meadow Pipit
  Anthus pratensis

Starling
  Sturnus vulgaris
Common Mynah
  Acridotheres tristis
Cowbird
  Molothrus ater
House Finch
  Carpodacus mexicanus
Greenfinch
  Chloris chloris
Goldfinch
  Carduelis carduelis
Chaffinch
  Fringilla coelebs
Vesper sparrow
  Pooecetes gramineus
Yellowhammer
  Emberiza citrinella

SELECTED BIBLIOGRAPHY

BARROWS, W. B. (1889). "The English sparrow (*Passer domesticus*) in North America." U.S. Dept. of Agric. Div. Orn. & Mamm. Bull. No. 1.

BARTHOLOMEW, G. A. (1949). "The effect of light intensity and day length on reproduction in the English sparrow." Bull. Mus. Comp. Zool. Harvard *101*, 433–76.

BAXTER, E. V. AND RINTOUL, L. J. (1953). The Birds of Scotland. Edinburgh.

BEER, J. R. (1961). "Winter feeding patterns in the house sparrow." Auk *78*, 63–71.

BERGTOLD, W. H. (1921). "The English sparrow (*Passer domesticus*) and the motor vehicle." Auk *38*, 244–50.

BEVEN, G. (1947). "Display of house sparrow." Brit. Birds *40*, 308–10.

BÖSENBERG, K. (1958). "Geschlechterverhältnis und Sterblichkeit der Nestlinge beim Haussperling (*Passer domesticus* L.)." Orn. Mitt. *10*, 86–8.

DAANJE, A. (1941). "Über das Verhalten des Haussperlings." Ardea *30*, 1–41.

DAVIS, J. (1953). "Precocious sexual development in the juvenal English sparrow." Condor *55*, 117–20.

DAVIS, J. AND DAVIS, B. S. (1954). "The annual gonad and thyroid cycles of the English sparrow in southern California." Condor *56*, 328–45.

EATON, W. F. (1924). "Decrease in English sparrows in eastern Massachusetts." Auk *41*, 604–6.

ELDER, H. F. D. (1949). "The appearance and disappearance of the house sparrow as a breeding species on the Isle of May." Scot. Nat. *61*, 101–3.

FALLET, M. (1958). "Der Jahresrhythmus eines grossstädischen Bestandes des Haussperlings (*Passer domesticus* L.)." Schriften Naturwiss. Ver. Schleswig-Holst. *29*, 39–46.

FALLET, M. (1958). "Zum Sozialverhalten des Haussperlings (*Passer domesticus* L.)." Zool. Anzeiger *161*, 178–87.

GEBHARDT, E. (1926). in review of "O Pardal Europeo (*Passer domesticus* L.). Estudo sobre sua divilgação, especialmente no Estado do Rio Grande do Sul." Egatea, Revista da Escola do Eugenharia de Porte Alegre. 1924, *9*, 1–8. Orn. Monatsb. *34*, 89–91.

GEBHARDT, E. (1959). "Europäische Vögel in überseeichen Ländern." Bonn zool. Beitr. *10*, 310–42.

GERSDORF, E. (1951). Sperlingsbekämpfung. Pflanzenschutz Hannover. Hamburg.

GREVE, K. (1958). "Zum Freibrüten der Haussperlinge (*Passer domesticus*) und des Feldsperlings (*Passer montanus*) auf Neuwerk." Orn. Mitt. *10*, 176.

GRIMM, H. (1954). "Biometrische Bemerkungen über mitteldeutsche und westdeutsche Sperlingspopulationen." J. Orn. *95*, 306–18.

GURNEY, J. H., RUSSELL, C., AND COUES, E. (1885). The House Sparrow. London.

HALLER, W. (1936). "Ein Beitrag zur Kenntnis der Verbreitung und Nistweise von Haus- und Feldsperling." Arch. Suisse d'Orn. *1*, 350–7.

HAMMER, M. (1948). "Investigations on the feeding habits of the house sparrow (*Passer domesticus*) and the tree sparrow (*Passer montanus*)." Danish Rev. Game Biology *1*, 1–59.

HOBBS, J. N. (1955). "House sparrow breeding away from man." Emu *55*, 302.

HUDSON, F. L. (1955). "Notes on the behaviour of juvenile house sparrows." Brit. Birds *48*, 459–60.

HUGHES, A. (1927). "Les moineaux dans la Gard." Rev. franc. d'Orn. *19*, 50–2.

KALMBACH, E. R. (1940). "Economic status of the English sparrow in the United States." U.S. Dept. Agric. Bull. No. 711.

KECK, W. N. (1932). "Control of the sex characters in the English sparrow, *Passer domesticus* (Linnaeus)." Proc. Soc. Exp. Biol. & Med. *30*, 158–9.

KENDEIGH, S. C. (1945). "Resistance to hunger in birds." J. Wildlife Management *9*, 217–26.

KIPPS, C. (n.d.). Sold for a Farthing. London.

KRÜGER, C. (1944). "En Undersøgelse af Graaspurvens (*Passer domesticus*) og Skovspurvens (P. montanus) Traek." Dansk Orn. Foren. Tids. *38*, 105–14.

LACK, D. (1940). "Variation in the introduced English sparrow." Condor *42*, 239–41.

LÖHRL, H. AND BÖHRINGER, R. (1957). "Untersuchungen an einer südwestdeutschen Population des Haussperlings (*Passer d. domesticus*)." J. Orn. *98*, 229–40.

LUND, Hj. MUNTHE-KAAS (1956). "Graspurven (*Passer domesticus* (L.)) i Nord-Norge." Dansk Orn. Foren. Tids. *50*, 67–76.

MANSFELD, K. (1950). "Beiträge zur Erforschung der wissenschaftlichen Grundlagen der Sperlingsbekämpfung." Nachr. Deutsch. Pflanzenschutzdienst *4*, 131–6, 147–54 and 164–75.

MAYR, E. (1949). "Enigmatic sparrows." Ibis *91*, 304–6.

MEISE, W. (1936). "Zur Systematik und Verbreitungsgeschichte der Haus- und Weidensperlinge, *Passer domesticus* (L.) und *hispaniolensis* (T.)." J. Orn. *84*, 631–72.

MOREAU, R. E. (1931). "An Egyptian sparrow roost." Ibis Ser. 13, *1*, 204–8.

NERO, R. W. (1951). "Pattern and rate of cranial 'ossification' in the house sparrow." Wilson Bull. *63*, 84–98.

NICHOLS, J. T. (1935). "Seasonal and individual variations in house sparrows." Bird Banding *6*, 11–15.

NIETHAMMER, G. (1953). "Gewicht und Flügellange beim Haussperling (*Passer d. domesticus*)." J. Orn. *94*, 282–9.

PIECHOCKI, R. (1954). "Statistiche Feststellungen an 20,000 Sperlingen (*Passer d. domesticus*)." J. Orn. *95*, 297–305.

POLIKARPOVA, E. (1940). "Influence of external factors upon the development of the sexual gland of the sparrow." Comptes Rendu (Doklady) Acad. Sci. U.R.S.S. *26*, 91–5.

PORTER, J. P. (1904). "A preliminary study of the psychology of the English sparrow." Am. J. Psychol. *15*, 313–46.

PORTER, J. P. (1906). "Further study of the English sparrow and other birds." Am. J. Psychol. *17*, 248–271.

PREISER, F. (1957). "Untersuchungen über die Ortstetigkeit und Wanderung der Sperlinge (*Passer d. domesticus* L.) als Grundlage für die Bekämpfung." Dissertation, Hohenheim, 1–57.

RADEMACHER, B. (1951). "Beringungsversuche über die Ortstreue der Sperlinge (*Passer d. domesticus* L. und *Passer m. montanus* L.)." Z. Pflanzenkrank. u. Pflanzenschutz *58*, 416–26.

RAND, A. L. (1956). "Changes in English sparrow population densities." Wilson Bull. *68*, 69–70.

SAGE, B. L. (1957). "Remarks on the taxonomy, history and distribution of the house sparrow introduced into Australia." Emu *57*, 349–52.

SCOTT, A. H. (1941). "News about sparrows." Avicultural Mag. (v), *6*, 50–7 and 94–101.

SEEL, D. C. (1960). "The behaviour of a pair of house sparrows while rearing young." Brit. Birds *53*, 303–10.

SICK, H. (1957). "Vom Hausspatzen (*Passer domesticus*) in Brasilien." Vogelwelt *78*, 1–18.

SICK, H. (1959). "A invasão da America Latina pilo pardal *Passer domesticus*, Linnaeus 1758, com referència especial ao Brasil." Boletim do Museu Nacional No. 207, 1–31.

SIMMONS, K. E. L. (1954). "Further notes on house sparrow behaviour." Ibis *96*, 478–81.

SOUTHERN, H. N. (1945). "The economic importance of the house sparrow, *Passer domesticus* L.: A review." Ann. Appl. Biol. *32*, 57–67.

STACHANOW, W. S. (1931). "Über die Verbreitung des Haussperlings im fernen Osten." J. Orn. *79*, 315–17.

STENHOUSE, J. H. (1928). "Remarkable decrease of the house sparrow in Fair Isle and Shetland." Scot. Nat. 162.

STONOR, D. (1939). "Parasitism of the English sparrow on the northern cliff swallow." Wilson Bull. *51*, 221–2.

THOMPSON, G. B. (1958). "The parasites of British birds and mammals. XXXIII. The insect ectoparasites of the house sparrow (*Passer d. domesticus* L.)." Ent. Monthly Mag. *94*, 1–5.

THREADGOLD, L. T. (1960). "A study of the annual cycle of the house sparrow at various latitudes." Condor *62*, 190–201.

VAURIE, C. (1956). "Systematic notes on palearctic birds. No. 24 Ploceidae: the genera *Passer*, *Petronia* and *Montifringilla*." Am. Mus. Nov. No. 1814.

WAGNER, H. O. (1959). "Die Einwanderung des Haussperlings in Mexiko." Z. Tierpsychol. *16*, 584–92.

WEAVER, R. L. (1939). "Winter observations and a study of the nesting of English sparrows." Bird Banding *10*, 73–79.

WEAVER, R. L. (1939). "The northern distribution and status of the English sparrow in Canada." Canad. Field Nat. *53*, 95–9.

WEAVER, R. L. (1942). "Growth and reproduction of English sparrows." Wilson Bull. *54*, 185–91.

WEAVER, R. L. (1943). "Reproduction in English sparrows." Auk *60*, 62–74.

WING, L. (1943). "The spread of the starling and the English sparrow." Auk *60*, 74–87.

THE HOUSE SPARROW

INDEX

INDEX